Table of Contents

LEVEL B

Table of Contents

LEVEL B

▶ Now try this!

Look at the letters and the picture in each box. Say the name of the picture.
If you hear the sound of the letter at the beginning, circle the letter on
the left. If you hear the sound at the end, circle the letter on the right.

1 s   s

2 d   d

3 g   g

4 h   h

5 f   f

6 p   p

7 r   r

8 m   m

9 k   k

10 y   y

11 t   t

12 j   j

13 w   w

14 b   b

15 n   n

▶ Here's what to do!

Say the name of each picture. Print the letter for its beginning sound.
Then print the letter for its ending sound. Trace the whole word.

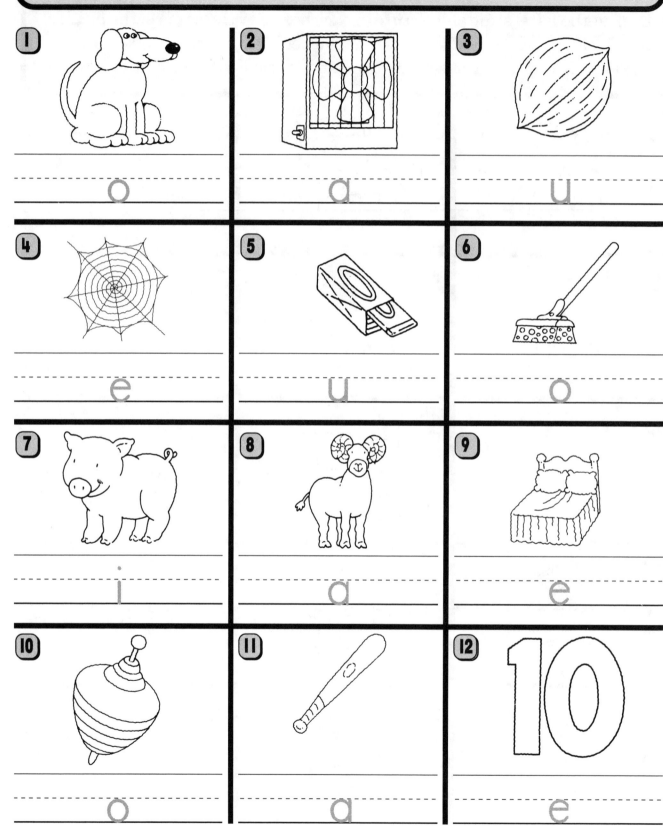

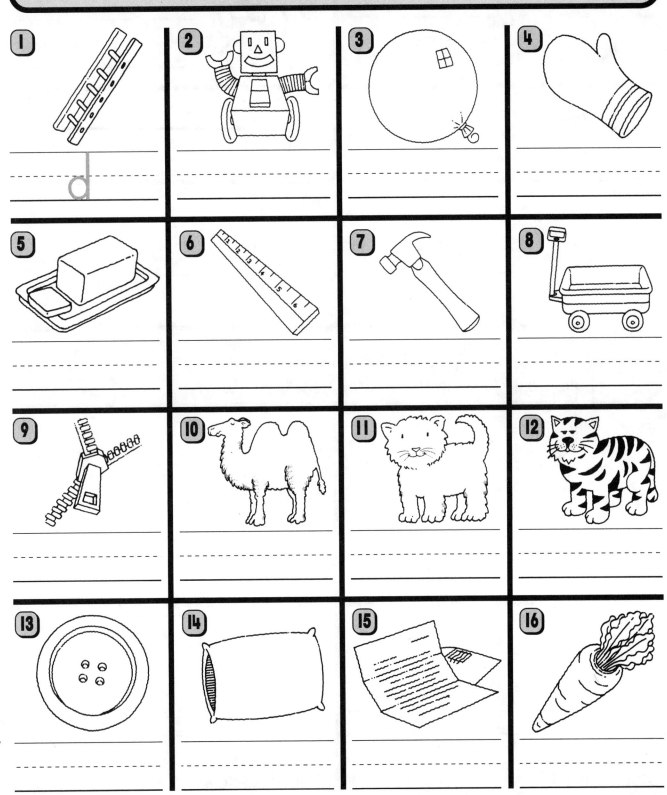

Here's what to do!

Say the name of each picture. Print the letter for its middle sound.

1. d
2.
3.
4.

5.
6.
7.
8.

9.
10.
11.
12.

13.
14.
15.
16.

Lesson 4: Medial consonants   **9**

Here's what to do!

Say the name of each picture. Print the letter for its middle sound. Trace the whole word.

1. ra io

2. spi er

3. ti er

4. pea ut

5. se en

6. ca el

Now try this!

Say the name of each picture. Print its missing letter on the line. Trace the whole word. Do what the sentences tell you to do.

7. dra on

Color it red.

8. ca in

Color it brown.

9. bo es

Color them blue.

10. le on

Color it yellow.

What kind of jam
can't you eat?

▶ **Here's what to do!**

Circle the name of each picture.

If a word or syllable has only one vowel, and it comes at the beginning or between two consonants, the vowel is usually short. You can hear the short **a** sound in **jam.**

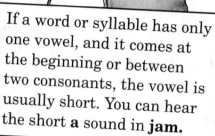

1
hat   ham

hand   had

2
bag   hat

bat   bad

3
camp   lad

lap   lamp

4
sad   back

bag   bat

5
cat   cap

cab   can

6
and   an

at   ant

7
mat   man

pan   map

8
cat   can

cab   cap

9
mad   ram

rack   mat

Answer: A traffic jam.

Lesson 6: Short vowel A

13

Circle the rhyming words in each box. Draw a picture of the word that does not rhyme.

1

cat
fan
hat
mat

2

Max
tax
bag
wax

3

cap
tap
map
cab

4

sack
hand
back
tack

5

bag
rag
cap
tag

6

sand
land
pan
band

7

ham
fan
ran
can

8

sad
bat
bad
had

9

quack
cat
sack
back

10

hand
land
lamp
sand

11

pan
fan
Dan
hat

12

sat
ax
pat
fat

▶ Here's what to do!

Print the name of each picture. Print a word that rhymes with it. Then do what the sentences tell you to do.

1	2	3	4

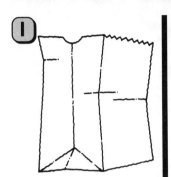 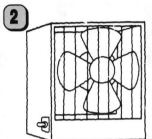 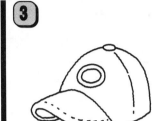 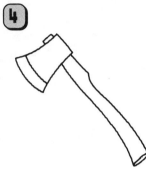

Color the bag red.

Color the fan green.

Color the cap red.

Color the ax blue.

5	6	7	8

  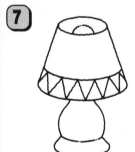 

Color the cat black.

Color the tack yellow.

Color the lamp green and blue.

Color the ram black and yellow.

Here's what to do!

Circle the word that will finish each sentence. Print it on the line.

1 I am Sam and my cat is _____ .   camp   Pat   cart

2 Pat likes milk and _____ food.   class   sat   cat

3 She eats a lot but she is not _____ .   van   fat   lamp

4 She likes to lick my _____ .   hand   gas   band

5 Pat likes to sit on my _____ .   lap   ham   Sam

6 Pat does not like to have a _____ .   gap   bath   rack

7 She runs away as _____ as she can.   fast   class   bass

8 I _____ always find her.   can   past   fast

9 She takes a nap on a _____ .   mast   mat   fat

10 She takes a _____ on Dad's lap.   ran   sat   nap

11 I _____ happy that Pat is my cat.   can   am   as

Little kitty visits the big city.

Here's what to do!

Circle the name of each picture.

If a word or syllable has only one vowel, and it comes at the beginning or between two consonants, the vowel is usually short. You can hear the short **i** sound in **kitty** and **big.**

1
sack
milk
mill
tap

2
mitt
fat
mat
mill

3
wind
tag
wig
wag

4
lap
lips
nap
dill

5
bag
pig
fig
pat

6
hill
bill
sill
hat

7
tax
six
fix
sat

8
bill
bit
hat
bib

9
wink
sank
sink
pink

Try this!

Color the parts of each ball with rhyming words the same color.

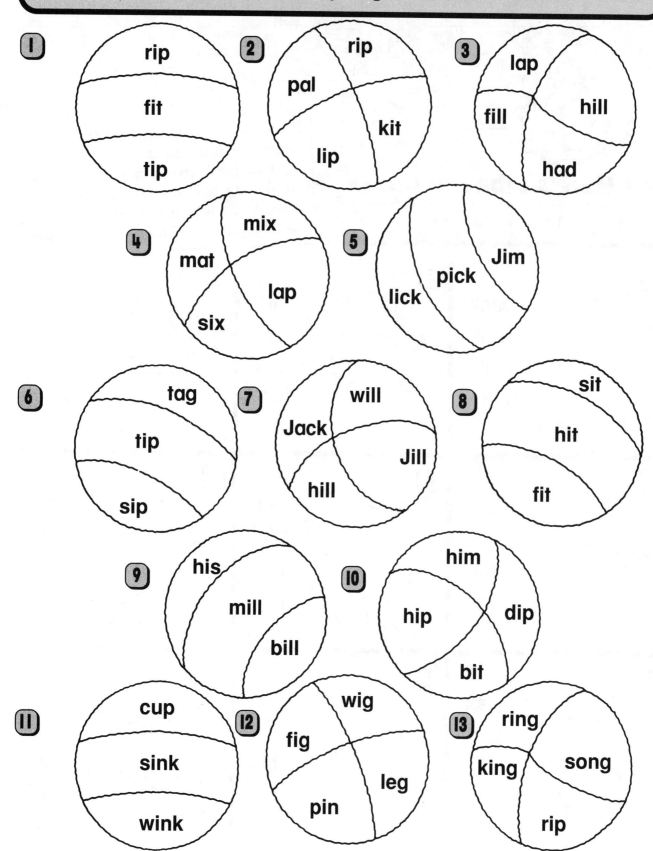

1. rip, fit, tip

2. rip, pal, kit, lip

3. lap, fill, hill, had

4. mix, mat, lap, six

5. Jim, pick, lick

6. tag, tip, sip

7. will, Jack, Jill, hill

8. sit, hit, fit

9. his, mill, bill

10. him, hip, dip, bit

11. cup, sink, wink

12. wig, fig, leg, pin

13. ring, king, song, rip

▶ Do it this way!

Print the name of each picture. Then print a word that rhymes with it.

1	2	3	4

5	6	7	8

9	10	11	12

Here's what to do!

Circle the word that answers each riddle. Print it on the line.

1 It can swim.
What is it?

_____
- - - - - - - - - -
_____

fast   fish
fix   fat

2 We drink it.
What is it?

_____
- - - - - - - - - -
_____

mitt   man
milk   mat

3 It comes after five.
What is it?

_____
- - - - - - - - - -
_____

sink   sad
sat   six

4 It rhymes with **bill**.
What is it?

_____
- - - - - - - - - -
_____

hit   hat
hill   ham

5 Lunch goes on it.
What is it?

_____
- - - - - - - - - -
_____

dad   dish
dig   did

6 It has a funny tail.
What is it?

_____
- - - - - - - - - -
_____

pin   pig
pal   pat

7 It fits on a finger.
What is it?

_____
- - - - - - - - - -
_____

rank   rat
rip   ring

8 A baby wears this.
What is it?

_____
- - - - - - - - - -
_____

bib   bad
bill   bat

9 We play ball with it.
What is it?

_____
- - - - - - - - - -
_____

mat   mitt
map   mix

Here's what to do!

Read the words that begin each sentence. Use all of the words on the right to finish the sentence. Print them on the lines.

1 _____

It is time to _____ .

a
trip
plan

---

2 _____

We will camp _____ .

Bill
Uncle
with

---

3 _____

Pam can _____ .

a
find
map

---

4 _____

Zack and Pam will _____ .

snacks
the
fix

---

5 _____

What will we pack _____ ?

in
bags
our

---

6 _____

Will our bags fit _____ ?

in
van
the

---

7 _____

Our dog Wags _____ .

will
tag
along

---

8 _____

The trip we take _____ .

fun
be
will

Lesson 10: Short vowels A and I

21

Here's what to do!

Circle the word that will finish each sentence. Print it on the line.

1 I am fishing _____ Uncle Jim.   ham   with   gift

2 We _____ to catch a basket of fish.   hand   fin   plan

3 I put a _____ worm on my hook.   hit   fat   tack

4 Soon a fish will _____ by.   dish   swim   mat

5 I feel a tug on my line at _____.   fast   last   bat

6 A fish just _____ my bait.   hat   fix   bit

7 It is so big I can hardly _____ it.   lid   limb   lift

8 Uncle Jim helps me pull it _____.   pan   in   fill

9 This _____ will make a nice big meal.   fish   wash   fins

10 We will cook it in a _____.   pan   list   past

11 We _____ make fish and chips.   can   cast   cups

12 We will put the fish on a _____.   inch   dish   ant

Snug as a bug in a rug.

►Here's what to do!

Circle the name of each picture. Print the vowel you hear in the word you circled.

If a word or syllable has only one vowel, and it comes at the beginning or between two consonants, the vowel is usually short. You can hear the short **u** sound in **bug** and **rug**.

1
cap   cup

kit   ___

2
gas   gull

gum   ___

3
Dick   duck

dad   ___

4
can   cup

cap   ___

5
as   bun

bus   ___

6
tug   tip

bug   ___

7
but   nut

nap   ___

8
sun   sum

dim   ___

9
tab   bin

bat   ___

Here's what to do!

Find the word in the box that names each picture. Print it on the line.

bun	cup	rug	bus	bug	sun
gum	hug	hut	tub	jug	duck

1.

2.

3.

4.

5.

6.

7.

8.

9.

10.

11.

12.

▶ Here's what to do!

Circle the word that answers each riddle. Print it on the line.

1 My name rhymes with **hug.** What am I?

bus   tub

bag   bug

2 I am good to eat. What am I?

big   bun

fun   run

3 This is fun to do. What is it?

just   lump

map   jump

4 You take a bath in me. What am I?

ran   tub

bun   rug

5 You can ride in me. What am I?

bud   big

bus   us

6 I shine on you. What am I?

sun   but

sit   fun

7 I say, "Quack, quack." What am I?

tack   luck

pup   duck

8 You can eat me. What am I?

cut   fit

fun   nut

9 We like to chew it. What is it?

just   bat

gum   must

Circle the word that will finish each sentence. Print it on the line.

1

Today there was a fuss on the _____ .

run
bus
must

2

A _____ jumped on Gus.

us
bug
hug

3

Gus jumped _____ .

run
cup
up

4

Then it jumped on _____ .

bus
hug
Russ

5

I saw the bug _____ on the window.

just
jump
rust

6

It was _____ a little bug.

just
cup
up

7

It liked to _____ up and down the window.

rug
run
cup

8

The bug _____ like to ride on the bus.

run
us
must

Try this!

Make new words by changing the vowels. Print them on the lines.

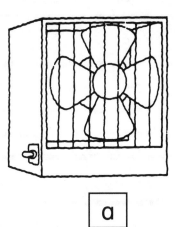  

a	i	u

1 fan — fin —

2 bad — —

3 ham — —

4 hat — —

5 as — —

6 bag — —

7 rag — —

8 bat — —

1 Can a cup run? ○ Yes ○ No

2 Is the sun black? ○ Yes ○ No

3 Can a cat run fast? ○ Yes ○ No

4 Can a big pig sing for you? ○ Yes ○ No

5 Can we nap in a tan van? ○ Yes ○ No

6 Can a man run up a hill? ○ Yes ○ No

7 Is a green rug red? ○ Yes ○ No

8 Can you sit on a bus? ○ Yes ○ No

9 Can a little pup run fast and jump? ○ Yes ○ No

10 Can you fill a pan with milk? ○ Yes ○ No

11 Can a doll jump on the bus? ○ Yes ○ No

12 Can a pig go as fast as a cab? ○ Yes ○ No

13 Can you rub your hands? ○ Yes ○ No

14 Is a happy cat sad? ○ Yes ○ No

15 Can a bus be big? ○ Yes ○ No

16 Can a bug sit in the mud? ○ Yes ○ No

17 Can a bug lift a bus? ○ Yes ○ No

18 Is a little doll as big as a bus? ○ Yes ○ No

Such A Rush!

This book belongs to

_____

1

✂

3

Nam runs down the hill as fast as he can.
The wind tugs at his cap.
"If I were a bug, this wind would lift me up," thinks Nam.

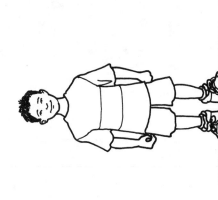

What will Nam wear the next time it rains?
Dress Nam for a rainy day.

8

Nam stands up. Mud is on his pants and his hands.
If I were a pig, I would like all this mud," thinks Nam.

6

Lesson 14: Fold-up Book: Reviewing short vowels A, I, U

29

2

"Hurry up, Nam!" says Dad. "Don't miss the bus."

Nam is in such a rush, he forgets his raincoat and umbrella.

4

Fat rain drops hit Nam and drip down his back.

"If I were a duck, I would like getting wet," thinks Nam.

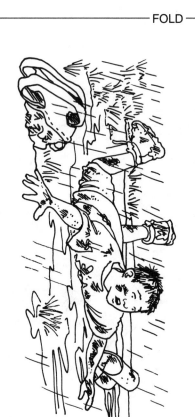

— FOLD —

— FOLD —

7

Nam is wet to the skin! "I'm not a bug or a duck.

I'm not a fish or a pig," he says. "I'm a wet, muddy kid.

Next time, I won't forget my raincoat and umbrella!"

5

Then, Nam slips on the slick path. Splat! He falls down in a mud puddle.

"If I were a fish, I could swim in this puddle," thinks Nam.

Pop goes the popcorn.
Pop, pop, pop!
Pop goes the popcorn.
Hot, hot, hot!

▶ Here's what to do!

Find the word in the box that names each picture. Print it on the line.

If a word or syllable has only one vowel, and it comes at the beginning or between two consonants, the vowel is usually short. You can hear the short **o** sound in **pop** and **hot**.

top	mop	pot	box	Tom	sock
hot	doll	fox	lock	rock	pop

▶ Do it this way!

Circle the name of each picture.

1
fix
cob
fox
six

2
pot
top
tap
pit

3
bill
sill
dill
doll

4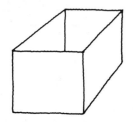
fox
fix
box
bat

5
dog
dug
dig
pot

6
rock
sit
sack
sock

7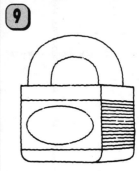
pig
pop
pup
pat

8
lag
log
bug
lot

9
luck
lock
lick
lack

10
mop
map
mud
milk

11
hat
hit
hot
hut

12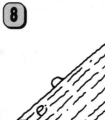
fix
tax
ax
ox

▶ **Try this!**

Fill in the bubble beside the sentence that tells about the picture. Then draw a box around each short **o** word in the sentences.

1
- ○ The fox is not on the log.
- ○ The fox is in the log.
- ○ The fox is on the log.
- ○ The fox is under the log.

2
- ○ Rob lost his socks.
- ○ Rob sat on a big rock.
- ○ Rob is on the big log.
- ○ Rob has a big rock in his hand.

3
- ○ The dog ran to the box.
- ○ The mop is not in the box.
- ○ I will hop on the log.
- ○ See the doll in the box.

4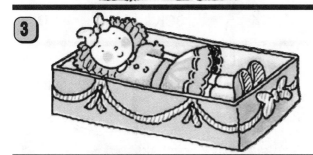
- ○ I got the mop for Don.
- ○ Jill has the big top.
- ○ The big top is on the mop.
- ○ The top is in Bob's hand.

5
- ○ The hot pot is on the table.
- ○ Dot is not holding a hot pot.
- ○ Dot is holding a hot pot.
- ○ The milk in the pot is not hot.

1 six   fix

sit   sun

2 bun   hit

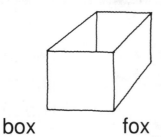

box   fox

3 tan   fan

fun   fin

4 cup   cap

kit   can

5 sick   sock

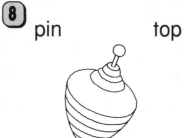

son   sack

6 rock   luck

lock   sock

7 fix   fox

box   fun

8 pin   top

pot   tip

9 pot   dug

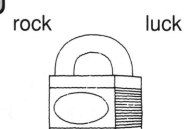

dog   log

10 hot   cot

pot   hut

11 rock   sock

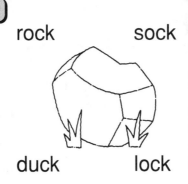

duck   lock

12 pig   pop

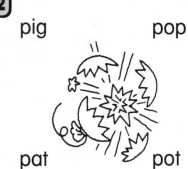

pat   pot

Here's what to do!

Print the name of each picture on the line.

 1

 2

3

4

5

6

7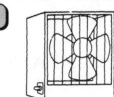

8

9

10

11

12

13

14

15

16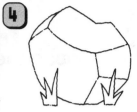

Do it this way!

Find the word in the box that will finish each sentence. Print it on the line.

1) Pam will make _____ for us.

2) Dot hopes she _____ make soup.

3) Bob wants _____ dogs.

4) Uncle _____ wants ham.

5) All the _____ want stew.

6) Let's _____ Pam what she made.

| Dan |
| kids |
| will |
| ask |
| hot |
| lunch |

7) _____ made a pot full of soup.

8) There is a wet _____ on the floor.

9) Dot _____ and can't stop.

10) She _____ the pot.

11) The soup spills _____ the floor.

12) Now Dot has to mop it _____ .

| spot |
| slips |
| Pam |
| on |
| up |
| drops |

36 Lesson 17: Reviewing short vowels A, I, U, O

What do you get when you wash your pet?

Try this!

Say the name of each picture. Print the name on the line.

If a word or syllable has only one vowel, and it comes at the beginning or between two consonants, the vowel is usually short. You can hear the short **e** sound in **get** and **pet.**

1 	2 	3 	4 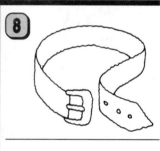
_____	_____	_____	_____

5 	6 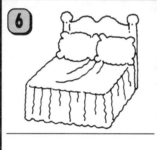	7 	8 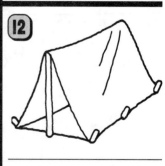
_____	_____	_____	_____

9 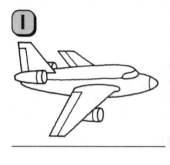	10 	11 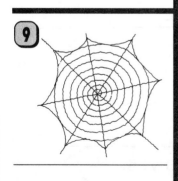	12 
_____	_____	_____	_____

Answer: Wet!

Lesson 18: Short vowel E

Here's what to do!

Print the name of each picture. Then do what the sentences tell you to do.

1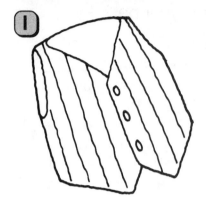

_____

- - - - - - - - - - - - - - - - - -

_____

2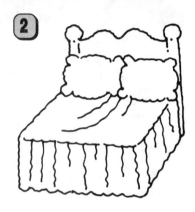

_____

- - - - - - - - - - - - - - - - - -

_____

Find the bed.
Color it red and blue.

Find the jet.
Color it black.

3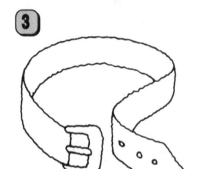

_____

- - - - - - - - - - - - - - - - - -

_____

4

_____

- - - - - - - - - - - - - - - - - -

_____

Find the nest.
Color three eggs red
and two eggs blue.

Find the tent.
Color it yellow.

5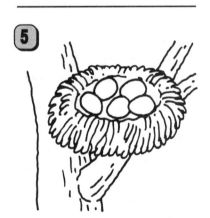

_____

- - - - - - - - - - - - - - - - - -

_____

6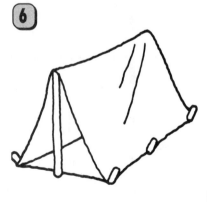

_____

- - - - - - - - - - - - - - - - - -

_____

Find the belt.
Color it green.

Find the vest.
Color it red and black.

Do it this way!

Fill in the bubble below the word that will finish each sentence.
Print it on the line.

1 My name is _____ .

men   Jeff   jet
○   ○   ○

2 I want to get a _____ .

bet   pet   yet
○   ○   ○

3 I would like a pet dog _____ .

rest   west   best
○   ○   ○

4 I will _____ take care of my pet.

help   bell   nest
○   ○   ○

5 I can take it to the _____ .

vet   bet   set
○   ○   ○

6 I will make sure it is _____ .

get   fed   bed
○   ○   ○

7 It will need a good _____ .

bed   nest   best
○   ○   ○

8 I will _____ it in and out.

jet   test   let
○   ○   ○

9 I can dry it when it's _____ .

net   wet   set
○   ○   ○

10 I will _____ it if I get it.

sled   pet   west
○   ○   ○

11 I might name my pet _____ .

Pepper   fed   set
○   ○   ○

12 I will _____ Ned about my pet.

sell   tell   fell
○   ○   ○

1	2	3	4	5
_____	_____	_____	_____	_____

▶ **Now try this!**

Answer each sentence by printing **yes** or **no** on the line.

6 You can rest in a bed.   _____

7 You have ten fingers and ten toes.   _____

8 A cat has six legs.   _____

9 A big bus can jump up and down.   _____

10 You can go fast in a jet.   _____

11 An ant is as big as an ox.   _____

12 Six is less than ten.   _____

13 You can sit in a tent.   _____

14 A hen can lay eggs.   _____

Here's what to do!

Find the word that will finish each sentence. Print it on the line.

1. A crab can dig in the _____ .

2. A hen sits on a _____ .

3. A _____ can live in a pen.

4. A spider spins a _____ .

5. A bug can be snug in a _____ .

6. A fish can _____ in the water.

nest
swim
rug
web
sand
pig

7. My _____ and I like to camp.

8. I help him _____ up the tent.

9. I sleep on my _____ .

10. My dad sleeps _____ a mat.

11. We have _____ when we camp.

on
cot
set
fun
dad

Look at each word. Change the vowel to make a new word. Print it on the line.

1 _____
tug _____

2 _____
tab _____

3 _____
fox _____

4 _____
rust _____

5 _____
sand _____

6 _____
tint _____

► **Now try this!**

Find the word that will finish each sentence. Print it on the line.

7 After the rain, the _____ was shining.

8 I _____ out to play and have fun.

9 I slid in the wet _____ .

10 I _____ and landed with a thud.

11 Now I am covered _____ mud.

12 It is time to _____ in the tub.

13 Then it will be time to go to _____ .

| hop |
| with |
| sun |
| fell |
| ran |
| mud |
| bed |

The Best Pet for You

This book belongs to

_____

3

Remember that a pet needs to be fed.
A big pet like a dog or a cat must be fed every day.
It needs fresh water to drink, too.

Write one or two sentences about your pet or a pet you would like to have.

_____

_____

_____

8

Pets can't sit still.
A dog needs to run and jump and romp.
A bird needs to fly.
A cat likes to play.

6

2

Kids have all kinds of pets.
What is the best pet for you?
Here are some things to think about
before you get a pet.

---- FOLD ----

4

A pet needs a snug home, too.
Fish need a tank. A rabbit needs a
hutch. A bird needs a cage.
A puppy or a kitten likes a soft bed.

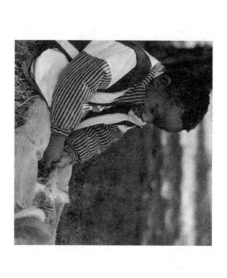

---- FOLD ----

7

If a pet gets sick, it may need to go to a vet.
Taking care of a pet is a big job.
It will need love and care all its life.

5

A pet's home must be kept clean.
A fish tank must be scrubbed.
A hamster cage needs to be cleaned.
A litter box needs to be kept fresh.

Lesson 21: Fold-up Book: Reviewing short vowels A, I, U, O, E

Jane wants the rain to stop today.
She wants to go outside and play.

Here's what to do!

Find the word that will finish each sentence. Print it on the line.

If a word or syllable has two vowels, the first vowel usually stands for the long sound, and the second vowel is silent. If the first vowel is **a,** the word has the long **a** sound. You can hear the long **a** sound in **Jane, rain,** and **play.**

1 Jane made a _____ when she saw it rain.

2 She wanted the rain to go _____ .

3 She had planned to _____ outside.

4 Then Jake _____ over.

5 Jake and Jane played _____ inside.

| away |
| face |
| games |
| came |
| play |

6 The children had to _____ for the rain to stop.

7 Jane's sister baked a _____ .

8 Jane and Jake _____ a piece.

9 At last the _____ stopped and they ran outside.

| rain |
| ate |
| wait |
| cake |

Circle the word that will finish each sentence. Print it on the line.

_____
- - - - - - - - - - - - - - - - - -

1 It is a nice _____ today.   day   rain   rake

- - - - - - - - - - - - - - - - - -

2 May we go to the _____ ?   bake   take   lake

_____
- - - - - - - - - - - - - - - - - -

3 Let's _____ a picnic lunch.   mail   take   say

_____
- - - - - - - - - - - - - - - - - -

4 We can bring a _____ and shovel.   pail   mail   rain

_____
- - - - - - - - - - - - - - - - - -

5 We could _____ sand castles.   make   wake   fake

_____
- - - - - - - - - - - - - - - - - -

6 Our dog _____ could come, too.   take   Kate   save

_____
- - - - - - - - - - - - - - - - - -

7 Is there any _____ we can go today?   say   tail   way

► **Now try this!**

Circle each long **A** word in the box. Then print the name of each picture on the line.

tap	tape	cap	cape	at	ate
mail	mat	rain	gate	hay	ham

8

_____
- - - - - - - - - - - - - - - - - -

9

_____
- - - - - - - - - - - - - - - - - -

10

_____
- - - - - - - - - - - - - - - - - -

11

_____
- - - - - - - - - - - - - - - - - -

I like pie.
Apple pie,
peach pie,
cherry pie.
I like pie.

> If a word or syllable has two vowels, the first vowel usually stands for the long sound, and the second vowel is silent. If the first vowel is **i**, the word has the long **i** sound. You can hear the long **i** sound in **like** and **pie.**

▶ Here's what to do!

Circle the name of each picture.

①	②	③	④

dim   dime | pig   pile | bike   big | bib   bite

▶ Now try this!

Circle the word that will finish each sentence. Then print it on the line.

⑤
Mike likes to ride a _____.

bit   bike   bite

⑥
Diane likes to _____.

hike   hill   hit

⑦
Ike likes cherry _____.

pie   pig   pine

⑧
Kyle likes to fly a _____.

bite   hive   kite

⑨
Fido likes to _____.

rid   ride   hive

⑩
We all like lunch _____.

tide   time   tip

▶ Here's what to do!

Circle the word that will finish each sentence. Print it on the line.

① A turtle can _____ inside its shell.   dime   time   hide

② A _____ can hide in a den very well.   lion   tile   pie

③ My dog can hide behind our _____ .   likes   bikes   dives

④ A bee can hide in its _____ .   hive   time   kite

⑤ A spider can hide anywhere it _____ .   pine   mine   likes

⑥ I _____ to hide things here and there.   like   mile   dime

⑦ No one can _____ them anywhere.   kind   find   pile

▶ Now try this!

Circle each long **I** word in the box. Print the name of each picture on the line.

dim	dime	pin	pine	rid	ride
mine	tie	sit	kite	nine	line

⑧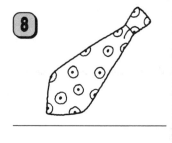

⑨

⑩

⑪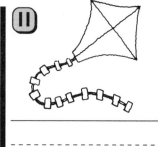

Sue and Luke are playing flutes.

Here's what to do!

Circle the answer **Yes** or **No** for each sentence. Then circle the long **U** word in each sentence. Print it on the line.

If a word or syllable has two vowels, the first vowel usually stands for the long sound, and the second vowel is silent. If the first vowel is **u,** the word has the long **u** sound. You can hear the long **u** sound in **Sue, Luke,** and **flutes.**

1 A red vase is blue. _____ Yes No

2 We can get toothpaste in a tube. _____ Yes No

3 A baby lion is a cube. _____ Yes No

4 A mule has nine tails. _____ Yes No

5 You stick things together with glue. _____ Yes No

6 We can eat a suit. _____ Yes No

7 A rule is a top that can sing. _____ Yes No

8 We play a song with a flute. _____ Yes No

9 We can hum a tune. _____ Yes No

Read the words in the box. Print the short **U** words under Short **U**.
Print the long **U** words under Long **U**.

cute	must	bug	duck
jump	suit	tune	bump
tube	dug	glue	mule
nut	rule	use	hum
flute	luck	jug	blue

Short U

Long U

The Duke Who Could Not Stay Awake

This book belongs to

_____

He slept while musicians with bagpipes, flutes, and lutes played a tune.

Draw a picture and write a sentence to tell what exercise will keep Luke awake.

"Duke Luke must stay awake," they said. "Let's use ice cubes!"

"STOP! I know what will help Luke stay awake," called a little girl. "He needs fresh air and exercise."

Lesson 27: Fold-up Book: Reviewing long vowels A, I, U

55

2

Once upon a time, there was a duke named Luke.
He could not stay awake.
He could not rule his land.

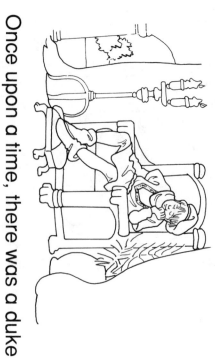

4

Bakers made huge plates of things for Luke to eat.
But nothing kept him awake.

FOLD

FOLD

And she was right!
Duke Luke ruled happily ever after.

7

They used a huge fan to make a breeze.
But still he slept.

5

I know a silly mole in an overcoat,
Who rows a very little boat.

Do it this way!

Circle each long **O** word in the box.

If a word or syllable has two vowels, the first vowel usually stands for the long sound, and the second vowel is silent. If the first vowel is **o**, the word has the long **o** sound. You can hear the long **o** sound in **know, mole,** and **boat.**

rod	road	rode	cot	coat	got	goat
hope	hop	robe	rob	row	cost	coast

Now try this!

Find the word in the box that will finish each sentence. Print it on the line.

1. Rover poked his _____ into his bowl.

2. He hoped to find a _____ .

3. There was no bone in his _____ .

4. Then along came his _____ , Joe.

5. Something was in the pocket of Joe's _____ .

6. Joe said, "I have something to _____ you."

7. Oh, boy! It was a bone for _____ !

coat
owner
Rover
show
bone
bowl
nose

Here's what to do!

Circle the name of each picture.

1	cot coat
2	toad tad
3	got goat
4	note not
5	sap soap
6	rope rot

Now try this!

Say the word in the box. Then read the sentence. To finish the sentence, think of a word that rhymes with the word in the box. Print the word on the line.

7 Joe was taking a ride in his _____.

8 Joe's dog Rover wanted to _____, too.

9 Rover poked Joe with his _____.

10 Joe told Rover to _____ into the boat.

11 Then Joe untied the _____.

12 Finally, Joe began to _____.

coat
no
rose
top
hope
bow

Water

This book belongs to

_____

We use water in our homes every day.
We need clean water for many things.

Can you think of other ways you can help save water?
Write a sentence telling how you can help.

_____

_____

Take shorter baths and showers.
Water plants and gardens in the morning or after the sun goes down.

2

Water comes from the rain and the snow that fills our lakes and streams.

FOLD

4

If there isn't enough rain or snow, our water supply grows smaller. That's why it's important not to waste water.

Following these simple tips will help you use water wisely every day.

FOLD

7

Here are some tips for how you can help save water: Don't leave the water running when you brush your teeth.

5

Name _____

We went to a baseball game,
And what did we do?
Ate peanuts and popcorn and ice cream, too!

 Do it this way!

Say the words in each box. Put two words together to make new words. Print the new words on the lines.

A **compound word** is made up of two or more words joined together to make a new word. **Popcorn** is corn that you pop.

1
pea	weed
sea	nut

peanut
_____

2
meal	oat
my	self

_____
_____

3
cup	rain
coat	cake

_____
_____

4
be	rail
road	may

_____
_____

5
base	class
mate	ball

_____
_____

6
pack	corn
back	pop

_____
_____

Lesson 34: Vowels in compound words   **69**

Look at the picture. Read the two words below it. Put them together to make one new word that names the picture. Print the new word on the line to finish the sentence.

①
mail + box

A box for mail is a _____.

②
rain + coat

A coat for rain is a _____.

③
back + pack

A pack for your back is a _____.

④
sail + boat

A boat with a sail is a _____.

⑤
pop + corn

Corn that can pop is _____.

⑥
sand + box

A box full of sand is a _____.

⑦
cup + cake

A cake in a cup is a _____.

Name _____

The spotted snake slid slowly down the slippery slide.

Here's what to do!

Say the name of each picture. Find its beginning blend in the box. Print it on the line.

Remember that in a **consonant blend** the sounds of the consonants blend together, but each sound is heard. You can hear **s** blends in **spotted, snake,** and **slid.**

sc	st	sp	sn	squ
scr	str	sl	sm	sw

1
_____

2
_____

3
_____

4
_____

5
_____

6
_____

7
_____

8
_____

9
_____

10
_____

11
_____

12
_____

▶ Do it this way!

Find a word in the box to finish each sentence. Print it on the line.

1 Did you ever _____ to think about snakes?

2 Snakes have long, _____ bodies.

3 Snakes can move both fast and _____ .

4 _____ have no arms or legs.

5 They still have the _____ to move.

6 Snakes can even _____ .

7 Their _____ looks slimy, but it's dry.

8 Snakes _____ some people, but not me.

scare
slim
skin
stop
skill
Snakes
swim
slow

▶ Now do this!

Circle the name of each picture.

9 	10 	11 
wim stem	scream screen	smile smoke
12 	13 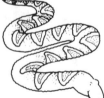	14 
sto steps	snake sneak	sled slide

Name _____

I like to jump,
I like to swing.
I like to run,
I like to sing.

▶ **Give this a try!**

Circle the word that
answers each riddle. Print it on the line.

Remember that in a
consonant blend the
sounds of the consonants
blend together, but each
sound is heard. You can
hear blends at the end of
jump and **sing.**

---

1 All mail needs
these. What are
they?

stamps   stumps

_____

2 We can ride on it.
What is it?

string   swing

_____

3 An elephant has
one. What is it?

skunk   trunk

_____

4 We can eat it.
What is it?

toast   list

_____

5 It hides your face.
What is it?

task   mask

_____

6 We can sleep in it.
What is it?

tent   plant

_____

7 We have two of
these. What are
they?

lands   hands

_____

8 Fish swim in it.
What is it?

tank   wink

_____

9 It can float.
What is it?

raft   left

_____

Here's what to do!

Find the word in the box that names each picture. Print it on the line.

milk	skunk	tent	belt	trunk	plants
nest	ring	stamp	raft	desk	tusk

1

_____

2

_____

3

_____

4

_____

5

_____

6

_____

7

_____

8

_____

9

_____

10

_____

11

_____

12

_____

Name _____

 Try this!

Find the missing word for each sentence by changing the blend of the word beside it to make a new word. Print it on the line. Use the blends in the box to help you.

sk	sp	tr	dr	str	br
fr	gl	sl	fl	pl	bl

1 I went to _____.

2 I had a strange _____.

3 The grass changed from green to _____.

4 The _____ was full of cows saying, "Boo!"

5 A _____ was full of cotton candy.

6 It _____ in the wind.

7 A big green _____ went flying past me.

8 I jumped out of bed in a _____.

9 My _____ had goose bumps.

10 My head was in a _____.

11 I dumped a _____ of water on top of me.

12 The dream did _____ tricks on me.

creep

scream

clown

sleet

free

flew

slog

crash

spin

grin

class

clay

1. I liked to play with my _____ ain _____.　　　　**fr　br　tr**

2. We like to climb _____ ees _____.　　　　**tr　fr　br**

3. Sometimes we _____ im _____ in the pool.　　　　**cr　sc　sw**

4. Sometimes we fish in a _____ eam _____.　　　　**str　fr　tr**

5. We like to _____ end _____ time together.　　　　**sp　sm　sn**

▶ Now do this!
Find a word in the box to finish each sentence. Print it on the line.

6. We saw a green _____.

7. It was very _____.

8. The frog _____ up onto a lily pad.

9. The lily pad _____ on a stream.

10. The _____ flowed through the woods.

11. Soon the frog jumped in the stream for a _____.

| small |
| swim |
| frog |
| stream |
| floated |
| climbed |

Name _____

See my little cherry tree,
With a rosy cherry just for me.
Won't you try my tasty treat?
A better snack you'll never eat!

▶ Give this a try!

Circle each word in which **Y** has a long **E** sound.

Sometimes **y** can stand for the vowel sound of long **e** or long **i**. You can hear the long **e** sound in **cherry**.

baby	cry	happy	why
try	every	hurry	tiny
Molly	sandy	shy	puppy
penny	Freddy	funny	bunny

▶ Now try this!

Circle the words in the sentences in which **Y** has a long **E** sound.

1. Ty and Molly were helping take care of baby Freddy.

2. They heard Freddy cry in his crib.

3. They went to help in a hurry.

4. They had to try everything to make him happy.

5. Ty read him a funny book about fish that fly.

6. Molly gave him her bunny to play with.

7. Ty made very silly faces.

8. Finally Freddy was happy.

Here's what to do!

Circle each word with a **Y** that sounds like long **I**.

When **y** is the only vowel at the end of a one-syllable word, **y** usually has the long **i** sound. You can hear the long **i** sound in **try**.

try	Freddy	sly	buggy	funny
bunny	dry	silly	rocky	my
Ty	windy	by	sky	sunny
sleepy	fly	happy	muddy	cry
sneaky	lucky	shy	puppy	Molly
why	jolly	baby	fry	very

Now do this!

Circle each word with **Y** that sounds like long **I** in the sentences.

1. Why do onions make us cry when we are happy?

2. Why is the sky blue on a sunny day?

3. Why do bats fly at night?

4. Why is a desert dry and a swamp muddy?

5. Why can a bird fly but not a puppy?

6. Why do we look silly if we try to fly?

7. Why is a fox sneaky and sly?

8. Why is a bunny shy?

9. Why does a rainy sky make you sleepy?

10. Do you ever wonder why?

Name _____

Read the word in each paw print. If the **Y** stands for a long **I** sound, color it yellow. If it stands for a long **E** sound, color it orange.

cry   bunny   sorry   my   Yuppy

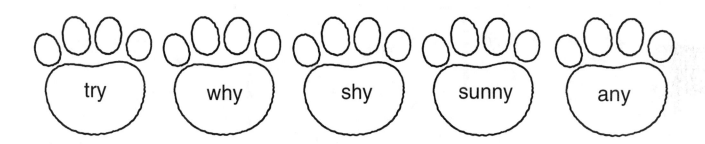

try   why   shy   sunny   any

Now try this!

Find a word from the top of the page to finish each sentence. Print it on the line.

1 _____ the puppy was digging a hole.

2 Suddenly he heard a _____ from inside.

3 A very angry _____ popped out of the hole.

4 "Why are you digging up _____ happy home?"

5 Yuppy yapped, "Oh, my! I'm very _____ ."

6 "I'll _____ to help you fix it up!"

Here's what to do!

Say the name of each picture. Circle each word that has the same sound of **Y** as the picture name.

1 	baby my fly fifty funny	**2**  sky sunny fairy cry Bobby	**3**  dolly try sly kitty dry

1
baby
my
fly
fifty
funny

2
sky
sunny
fairy
cry
Bobby

3
dolly
try
sly
kitty
dry

4
lady
penny
shy
fry
happy

5
why
silly
lily
by
bunny

6
my
sixty
fly
Sally
sky

7
jelly
Sandy
my
fry
cry

8
lucky
try
fifty
sky
puppy

9
berry
very
try
sly
any

10
cry
lady
many
sky
by

11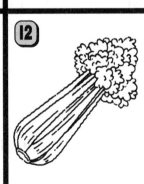
only
city
July
spy
funny

12
my
fly
fifty
happy
silly

Name _____

When sitting in her chair each night,
Beth sees the stars shining so bright.

▶ Do it this way!

Circle the word that will finish each sentence. Print it on the line.

A **consonant digraph** is two consonants that together stand for one sound. You can hear consonant digraphs in **when, chair, the,** and **shine.**

1 I go to the zoo to see the _____.   chop   chimp   check

2 It smiles to show its _____.   then   teeth   these

3 They are big and _____.   which   what   white

4 It eats bananas by the _____.   bunch   reach   much

5 Once I saw it eat a _____.   that   ship   peach

6 Sometimes it dumps its _____.   wish   dish   swish

7 Then it naps in the _____.   fresh   shut   shade

▶ Now do this!

Find two words from the top of the page that begin with **ch, wh, th,** and **sh**. Print them on the lines beside the correct consonant digraph.

8 _____

ch _____

9 _____

th _____

10 _____

wh _____

11 _____

sh _____

▶ Do it this way!

Fill in the bubble beside the word that will finish each sentence. Print it on the line.

1 Chip and I didn't know _____ to go.

○ where
○ what

2 We decided to go to the mall to _____.

○ chop
○ shop

3 They sell everything _____.

○ this
○ there

4 There was so _____ to choose from.

○ catch
○ much

5 I couldn't decide _____ I wanted most.

○ what
○ who

6 Then I saw some model _____ kits.

○ shirt
○ ship

7 _____ was what I wanted most.

○ When
○ That

8 I _____ a clipper ship to make.

○ chose
○ chair

9 _____ chose a spaceship kit.

○ Choose
○ Chip

10 _____ we had lunch.

○ Then
○ That

11 A little _____ later, we went home.

○ while
○ what

12 I put together my ship _____ night.

○ then
○ that

Name _____

 Give this a try!

Say each word in the box. If the consonant digraph is at the beginning of a word, print the word in the first column. If it is in the middle, print the word in the second column. If it is at the end, print the word in the third column.

cheer	quack	thank	stuck	while	teacher	brother
when	father	kicking	peach	dishes	cracker	what
bath	wishing	fish	thin	beach	why	wash
chin	clothes	shell	touch	mother	reach	

Beginning	**Middle**	**End**
_____	_____	_____
_____	_____	_____
_____	_____	_____
_____	_____	_____
_____	_____	_____
_____	_____	_____
_____	_____	_____

Say the name of each picture. Circle the consonant digraph you hear.

1		2		3		4	
	th		th		th		th
	sh		sh		sh		sh
	ck		ck		ck		ck
	ch		ch		ch		ch
	wh		wh		wh		wh

5		6		7		8	
	th		th		th		th
	sh		sh		sh		sh
	ck		ck		ck		ck
	ch		ch		ch		ch
	wh		wh		wh		wh

9		10		11		12	
	th		th		th		th
	sh		sh		sh		sh
	ck		ck		ck		ck
	ch		ch		ch		ch
	wh		wh		wh		wh

13		14		15		16	
	th		th		th		th
	sh		sh		sh		sh
	ck		ck		ck		ck
	ch		ch		ch		ch
	wh		wh		wh		wh

Lesson 48: Test: Consonant digraphs SH, TH, WH, CH, CK

Name _____

Who is in that suit you see?
It's a knight with knocking knees.

▶ **Give this a try!**

Read each sentence. Find the picture it tells about.
Write the sentence letter under the picture.

You can hear the
consonant digraph
kn in **knight,
knocking,** and
knees.

1
a. John has a knot in the rope.
b. I know what is in the box.
c. Joan turned the knob.

_____   _____

2
a. Theo will knock down the pile.
b. Mom cut it with a knife.
c. Joe knocks on the door.

_____   _____

3
a. The knight wore armor.
b. Tad's knee needs a patch.
c. Grandma likes to knit.

_____   _____

▶ **Now try this!**

Find a word in the box that answers each riddle. Print it on the line.

4 Something that can cut. _____

5 Someone who wore armor. _____

6 Something you can tie. _____

| knife |
| knot |
| knight |

Circle the word that will finish each sentence. Print it on the line.

1 I _____ how to do many things. know knot

2 I can spread butter with a _____. knot knife

3 I can touch my _____ to my chin. knees knew

4 I can tie _____. knots knits

5 I can turn a door _____. knee knob

6 I can read about _____. know knights

7 I can _____ a sweater. knit knife

8 I've _____ how to do these things for a long time. knit known

Now do this!

Think of a word that begins with **kn** and rhymes with each word. Print it on the line.

9 snow

10 block

11 wife

_____

12 blew

13 see

14 hot

_____

15 own

16 sit

17 sob

_____

Name _____

Can you whistle?
I can, too.
Listen now
And I'll whistle for you.

 Here's what to do!

Find the word in the box that names each picture. Print it on the line.

apple	eagle	people
candle	buckle	whistle
turtle	bottle	table

1

_____

2

_____

3

_____

4

_____

5

_____

6

_____

7

_____

8

_____

9

_____

Do it this way!

Find the word that will finish each sentence. Print it on the line.

1. A _____ uses its own shell for a house.

2. It can swim in a small _____ .

3. It can _____ around in the puddle.

4. It can climb on rocks and _____ .

5. An _____ might fly over and scare it.

6. Sometimes _____ may scare it, too.

7. Then the turtle can _____ safely in its shell.

| pebbles |
| eagle |
| people |
| turtle |
| huddle |
| puddle |
| paddle |

8. I have a _____ pet turtle.

9. My _____ gave it to me.

10. It's not even as big as a _____ .

11. I named my turtle _____ .

12. When I hold it, its feet _____ my hand.

13. Then I laugh and _____ .

14. Sometimes, it sits on the _____ next to my bed.

| giggle |
| table |
| little |
| Wiggle |
| pickle |
| tickle |
| uncle |

102 Lesson 50: Words ending in LE

Name _____

I wrote a poem yesterday
About the fun on my birthday.
I got a great big gift, you know,
that was all wrapped up with a bow.

▶ **Give this a try!**

Find the word in the box that will finish each sentence. Print it on the line.

You can hear the consonant digraph **wr** in **wrote** and **wrapped.**

wren	wreck	wrap	wrestle	write
wrist	wrench	wrecker	wrong	wriggle

1 To move around is to _____.

2 The opposite of **right** is _____.

3 A small bird is a _____.

4 A thing that is ruined is a _____.

5 To hide a gift in paper is to _____ it.

6 When you put a story on paper you _____.

7 Your _____ holds your hand to your arm.

8 A truck that clears away wrecks is a _____.

9 A kind of tool is a _____.

10 One way to fight is to _____.

Find a word in the box that answers each riddle. Print it on the line.

wren	wrecker	wriggle	wrap	wrist
wrench	wreath	writer	typewriter	wrinkle

1 I am round and pretty.
You can hang me up.
What am I?

_____

2 I hide a gift.
You tear me up.
What am I?

_____

3 I can fly.
I like to sing.
What am I?

_____

4 I am a useful tool.
I can fix things.
What am I?

_____

5 I am next to a hand.
I can twist and bend.
What am I?

_____

6 I can print.
People press my keys.
What am I?

_____

7 I am a big truck.
I tow things away.
What am I?

_____

8 I write stories. They can be
real or make believe.
What am I?

_____

9 I am a fold in a dress.
I am a crease in a face.
What am I?

_____

10 I am another word for **squirm.**
I rhyme with **giggle.**
What am I?

_____

Name _____

▶ Do it this way!

Find the word in the box that will finish each sentence. Print it on the line.

1 I like to read stories _____ about knights.

2 _____ lived a long time ago.

3 They _____ themselves in metal armor.

4 It was the only way they _____ to protect themselves.

5 Armor gloves protected the knights' hands and

_____.

6 The legs of the armor bent at the _____.

7 I'd like to _____ more about wearing armor.

8 Did metal armor ever get _____?

9 Could a knight get up if he were _____ off a horse?

10 I wonder if knights _____ inside their armor!

11 I'll find out all I can and _____ a report about it.

knocked
know
knuckles
Knights
write
wriggled
wrapped
written
knees
wrecked
knew

Say the name of each picture. Print the consonant digraphs where you hear them in the words. Some words will have two consonant digraphs.

Name _____

Find the word that answers each riddle. Print its letter on the line.

1 A bike rolls on them. _____ **a.** sheep

2 It gives us wool. _____ **b.** brush

3 It is something we use for our hair. _____ **c.** whale

4 It can blow air and water from a hole in its head. _____ **d.** wheels

5 This is used to cut things. _____ **e.** knife

_____

6 We use a pencil to do this. _____ **a.** teeth

7 It is not fair to do this. _____ **b.** rattle

8 This is a chair fit for a king. _____ **c.** cheat

9 These show when we smile. _____ **d.** throne

10 Wind makes a door do this. _____ **e.** write

_____

11 These are fun to find on the beach. _____ **a.** whisper

12 These taste good. _____ **b.** peaches

13 This is a quiet way to talk. _____ **c.** shells

14 Smoke goes up this. _____ **d.** clock

15 This tells us the time. _____ **e.** chimney

Say the name of each picture. Print its missing letters on the line. Trace the whole word.

1. ___eese

2. ___ell

3. ___app

4. ___ock

5. ___ite

6. tru___

7. di___es

8. cand___

9. ___eel

10. turt___

11. ___irty

12. ___erry

Name _____

On the farm, in a barn,
Animals live safe from harm.

▶ Here's what to do!

Find the word in the box that will finish each sentence. Print it on the line.

An **r** after a vowel makes the vowel have a sound that is different from the usual short or long sound. You can hear the **ar** sound in **barn, farm,** and **harm**.

apart	star	hard
part	car	hardly
start	large	jars

1 I picked out a new model _____ kit.

2 I got two _____ of paint, too·

3 I could hardly wait to _____ on it.

4 I glued it so the car wouldn't fall _____.

5 There were small parts and _____ parts.

6 The tires were _____ to fit, but I did it.

7 I stuck gold _____ stickers on the sides.

8 I could _____ believe it when it was done.

9 The best _____ was showing it to my friends.

Finish each sentence. Use a word that rhymes with the word beside the sentence. Print it on the line.

1 A shark is a very _____ animal.

part

2 It lives in the deep, _____ part of the ocean.

bark

3 It can grow to be very _____ .

barge

4 A shark's teeth are very _____ .

carp

5 It has no problem tearing food _____ .

start

6 I live _____ from the ocean where sharks live.

star

7 I like to visit the animal _____ .

lark

8 It's not _____ from my house.

car

9 I can watch the sharks there free from _____ .

farm

Now do this!

Print three rhyming words under each word.

10   mark   11   start   12   hard

_____ | _____ | _____

_____ | _____ | _____

_____ | _____ | _____

Name _____

My ears are good for you to eat,
with a fork or in your hands.
What am I?

> ### ▶ Here's what to do!
>
> Read each riddle. Answer it with a word that rhymes with the word beside the riddle. Print it on the line.

Remember that an **r** after a vowel makes the vowel have a sound that is different from the usual short or long sound. You can hear the **or** sound in **for** and **fork.**

1 Something we can pop and eat. _____ | horn |

2 Something on a unicorn. _____ | born |

3 Something we eat with. _____ | cork |

4 Something with rain, wind, and thunder. _____ | form |

5 Something we can play or watch. _____ | port |

6 Something sharp on a rose. _____ | born |

7 Something beside the sea. _____ | tore |

8 Something to close up a bottle. _____ | pork |

9 Something that gives us light. _____ | porch |

Answer: Corn.

Lesson 55: The sound of OR **111**

Now try this!

Circle the name of each picture.

1

home

horse

horn

2

arm

are

am

3

barn

bark

book

4

home

horse

horn

5

40

fifty

forty

fairy

6

torch

tar

scorch

7

car

card

cost

8

come

corn

cart

9

store

stand

star

10

horn

thirty

thorn

11

car

jar

jam

12

scarf

scare

scorn

112 Lesson 55: Reviewing AR and OR

Sparky the Shark

This book belongs to

─── FOLD ───

Sparky's mother tried to teach him.
"Stay in this part of the sea," she said.
"Don't swim too close to the shore."

─── FOLD ───

Print what Sparky and his mother said to each other after she brought him

8 home.

The force of the storm drove Sparky onto a sand bar.
When the storm ended, Sparky was worn out.

6 He was far, far from home.

Lesson 56: Fold-up Book: Reviewing AR, OR

113

2

Sparky the shark was born in a large harbor.

He never swam far from his mother.

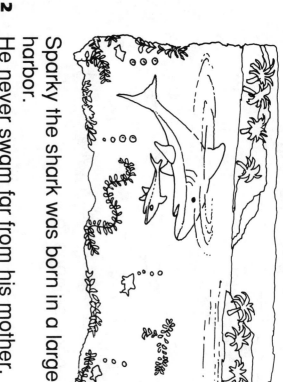

4

As Sparky got older, he forgot her warning.

He swam off to explore.

He swam toward the shore.

FOLD

Sparky's mother found him and led him home.

Sparky never forgot the storm.

He stayed close to his mother forever more.

7

FOLD

Just then, a horrible storm began.

The sea grew dark.

Sparky was tossed around like a cork on the waves.

5

Name _____

It's sometimes shaped liked a circle.
It's the home of a turtle and other animals.
What is it?

 **Give this a try!**

Circle each word that has the
same vowel sound as the name
of the picture.

Remember that an **r** after a vowel
makes the vowel have a sound that is
different from the usual short or long
sound. You can hear the **ir** sound in
circle, the **ur** sound in **turtle**, and the
er sound in **other**.

1 | **ir** | first
                    fork
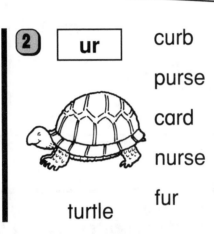   skirt
                    shirt
          bird   girl

2 | **ur** | curb
                    purse
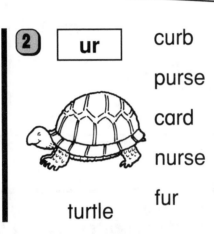   card
                    nurse
          turtle   fur

3 | **er** | batter
                    letter
       hammer
                    park
          fern   clerk

 Now try this!

Find the name of each picture in the words above. Print each name on
the lines.

4 | **5** | **6** | **7**

_____ | _____ | _____ | _____

8 | **9** | **10** | **11**

_____ | _____ | _____ | _____

Answer: A shell.

Do it this way!

Circle the name of the picture. Color the box with the same vowel with **r.**

1	bird barn burn

er	or	ir

2	first batter farm

ir	er	ar

3	tar turtle third

ur	ar	or

4	hammer farmer summer

ir	or	er

5	shirt skirt scarf

ar	ir	ur

6	goat garden girl

ir	or	ur

Now do this!

Circle the word that will finish the sentence. Print it on the line.

7 Cats have _____ and purr.   far   fur

8 Birds have feathers and _____.   cheat   chirp

9 Turtles _____ up inside their shells.   curl   car

10 Fish have fins and swim in the _____.   river   hurt

11 Worms wiggle and live in _____.   burn   dirt

12 Have you _____ wondered why?   other   ever

116 Lesson 57: The sound of IR, ER, UR

Name _____

▶ Here's what to do!

Find the vowel followed by **r** in each word. Print the two letters on the line. Then print the number of the picture with the same two letters.

1 car   **2** horn   **3** bird   **4** hammer   **5** turtle

1 part _____ ____

2 verse _____ ____

3 turn _____ ____

4 pork _____ ____

5 first _____ ____

6 party _____ ____

7 third _____ ____

8 bark _____ ____

9 fern _____ ____

10 storm _____ ____

11 her _____ ____

12 chirp _____ ____

13 park _____ ____

14 horse _____ ____

15 fur _____ ____

16 skirt _____ ____

17 curb _____ ____

18 short _____ ____

19 purse _____ ____

20 under _____ ____

21 hard _____ ____

22 burn _____ ____

Circle the letters that will finish the word in each sentence. Print them on the line. Trace the whole word.

1 Many different things happen in sp___ts.   er   or   ir

2 A diver jumps in the water head f___st.   ur   ir   ar

3 A s___fer stands up on the ocean waves.   ar   or   ur

4 A ski jump___ glides off high cliffs.   ir   er   ur

5 There ___e some sports I like to play.   or   er   ar

6 There are oth___ I'd rather watch.   ar   ir   er

7 Socc___ is a game I like to play.   ir   ur   er

8 Tennis is a game I'd rath___ watch.   ar   or   er

► **Now try this!**

Use the words in the box to answer the riddles.

bark	skirt	car	park	fur	corn

9 It is part of a dress.

10 You like to eat it.

11 Dogs make this noise.

_____

12 A rabbit has it.

13 A person can drive it.

14 We play games in it.

_____

Name _____

► Here's what to do!

Say the name of each picture. Fill in the bubble beside its vowel with **r**.

1

○ ur
○ or
○ ar

2

○ ar
○ er
○ or

3

○ ar
○ er
○ or

4

○ er
○ or
○ ar

5
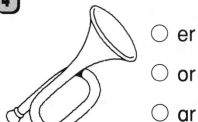
○ ar
○ er
○ or

6

○ or
○ ar
○ ir

7

○ ar
○ or
○ ir

8

○ or
○ ur
○ ar

9

○ ir
○ or
○ ar

10
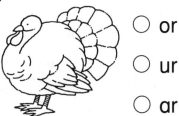
○ or
○ ur
○ ar

11
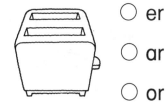
○ er
○ ar
○ or

12

○ ur
○ or
○ ar

Here's what to do!

Draw a line under each word in the sentences with **ar, or, ir, er,** or **ur.**
Then do what each sentence tells you to do.

1 Do you see the skirt? Circle the skirt. Color the skirt purple.

2 See the letter. Color it green. Make a black dot near it.

3 Can you see the fern? Color it green. Draw a line under it.

4 Find the turkey. Color its feathers orange and yellow.

5 See the barn. Make a little black **X** under it. Color the barn red.

6 Do you see the corn. Color the corn yellow. Draw a box around it.

7 See the star. Color it blue. Make two red dots near the star.

8 Look at the turtle. Make a blue **X** under it. Color it green and black.

9 Find the horse. Draw a line under it. Color the horse brown.

10 See the car. Draw a circle around it. Color it blue.

The Barn in Winter

This book belongs to

_____

The farmer's herd of cows are in the barn.
The farm horses stay warm in the barn, too.

What is winter like where you live?
Write a few sentences that tell about it.

8

The mice have a nest in a dark corner.
They hurry and scurry and gather corn to eat.

6

2

In Vermont, winter days are short.
Stormy winds are sharp and cold.
Who lives in this barn during the winter?

4

Turkeys and chickens live in part of the barn.
They don't mind the horses and cows nearby.

7

The barn cat sleeps in the corner.
She looks like a ball of fur.
Is she dreaming of warm weather?

5

Birds perch on beams high in the barn.
They fly in circles stirring up dirt.

Name _____

He'll get the broom,
then we'll clean our room.

▶ Do it this way!

Print a word from the box that means the same as the two words beside each line.

A **contraction** is a short way of writing two words. It is formed by putting two words together and leaving out one or more letters. An apostrophe (') is used to show where something is left out. Some contractions are formed with the word **will**.

we will = we'll

| you'll | they'll | she'll |
| we'll | I'll | he'll |

1 I will _____

2 he will _____

3 we will _____

4 they will _____

5 she will _____

6 you will _____

▶ Now do this!

Print the short form of the two underlined words in each sentence.

7 <u>I will</u> get in the boat and you'll get in, too. _____

8 <u>He will</u> climb aboard. _____

9 <u>She will</u> join us and jump in. _____

10 <u>They will</u> hop in for the ride. _____

11 All aboard? Oh, no! <u>We will</u> sink! _____

Print a word from the box that means the same as the two words beside each line.

Some contractions are formed with the word **not**.
does not = doesn't

can't	couldn't	weren't	doesn't	don't
didn't	aren't	isn't	won't	haven't

1 are not _____

2 do not _____

3 did not _____

4 will not _____

5 were not _____

6 is not _____

7 could not _____

8 can not _____

9 does not _____

10 have not _____

Now try this!

Print two words that mean the same as each underlined word.

11 Mitten the kitten <u>can't</u> get down from the tree.

_____

12 She <u>isn't</u> brave enough to climb down.

_____

13 She <u>doesn't</u> know what to do.

_____

14 We <u>haven't</u> any problem getting her down.

_____

15 "<u>Aren't</u> you a lucky kitten to have friends to help?"

_____

Name _____

**Do it this way!**

Circle two words in each sentence that can be made into one of the contractions in the box. Print the contraction on the line.

Some contractions are formed with the word **is**.
he is = he's

| he is = he's | That is = That's | it is = it's |
| she is = she's | It is = It's | |

1

It is Rocky's birthday. _____

2

What a surprise he is going to get! _____

3

Jess has his gift, but she is hiding it. _____

4

Do you think it is something Rocky wants? _____

5 What will Rocky get? Look at the picture at the top. That is what Rocky wants the most.

_____

▶ Here's what to do!

Print the contraction that means the same as the underlined words in each sentence.

Some contractions are formed with the word **have**.

You have = You've
I have = I've
We have = We've
They have = They've

1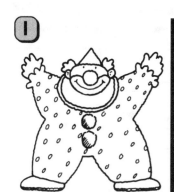

I have made you smile.

_____ made you smile.

2

We have shown you tricks.

_____ shown you tricks.

3

They have tossed a ball with their noses.

_____ tossed a ball with their noses.

4

You have had a good time.

_____ had a good time.

Name _____

 Give this a try!

Print two words that mean the same as the underlined word in each sentence.

Contractions can be formed using the words **am, are,** or **us.**
  I am = I'm
  we are = we're
  let us = let's

1. <u>Let's</u> have a party. _____

2. <u>We'll</u> ask our friends to come. _____

3. <u>I'm</u> going to pop popcorn. _____

4. <u>He's</u> going to bring some lemonade. _____

5. <u>She's</u> going to bring some cupcakes. _____

6. <u>They're</u> going to bring games. _____

7. <u>We're</u> going to have fun! _____

 Now try this!

Print the contraction that means the same as the two words beside the line.

8. you are _____   9. she is _____

10. I am _____   11. it is _____

12. let us _____   13. they are _____

14. we are _____   15. we will _____

16. he is _____   17. they will _____

18. I will _____   19. he will _____

Here's what to do!

Print the letter of each contraction next to the words that have the same meaning.

a. we're	**b.** you'll	**c.** it's	**d.** can't	**e.** I'm
f. he's	**g.** won't	**h.** let's	**i.** don't	**j.** she's
k. you're	**l.** isn't	**m.** he'll	**n.** we'll	**o.** I'll
p. I've	**q.** they'll	**r.** she'll	**s.** we've	**t.** aren't

1 _____ I am **2** _____ we are **3** _____ will not **4** _____ he is

5 _____ you will **6** _____ let us **7** _____ can not **8** _____ it is

9 _____ is not **10** _____ you are **11** _____ I will **12** _____ we will

13 _____ do not **14** _____ I have **15** _____ she will **16** _____ she is

17 _____ he will **18** _____ we have **19** _____ are not **20** _____ they will

Now do this!

Find a word in the box that will finish each sentence. Print it on the line.

21 _____ go skating in the park.

22 _____ time for us to go.

23 I _____ want to be late.

24 I know _____ ready now, are you?

25 _____ help you find your skates.

26 I think _____ going to have fun.

Let's
I'm
It's
I'll
don't
we're

▶ Give this a try!

Print two words that mean the same as each contraction.

1 I've _____   2 didn't _____

3 he'll _____   4 they've _____

5 you're _____   6 let's _____

7 isn't _____   8 won't _____

9 haven't _____   10 I'll _____

11 hasn't _____   12 they're _____

13 you'll _____   14 I'm _____

▶ Now try this!

Print the contraction for the underlined words in each sentence.

15 I have not heard Jake's story yet.   _____

16 He has not read it aloud.   _____

17 I can not wait to hear it.   _____

18 Now he will read his story to the class.   _____

19 Let us listen to him.   _____

20 You are a good reader, Jake.   _____

21 I will help you make a book from your story.   _____

Print the contraction for the two words beside each line.

1 I have _____

2 can not _____

3 do not _____

4 that is _____

5 let us _____

6 there is _____

7 did not _____

8 you have _____

9 she is _____

10 could not _____

Now do this!

Circle the contraction that will finish each sentence. Print it on the line.

11 _____ a surprise for Linda.   Didn't   It's

12 _____ her new bike.   That's   Isn't

13 She _____ guess what it is.   won't   you're

14 She _____ think she'll get one.   aren't   doesn't

15 _____ here now!   She's   You'll

16 "Linda, _____ going to show you something."   we're   don't

17 "_____ be very surprised!"   There's   You'll

Name _____

I'll have one peach for lunch.   Here are some peaches for my pals to munch.

▶ **Here's what to do!**

Circle the word that will finish each sentence. Print it on the line. Color one or more pictures in each box to match the answer.

When **s** or **es** is added to a word it forms the plural. Plural means "more than one." If a word ends in **x, z, ss, sh,** or **ch,** usually add **es** to make it mean more than one. For other words just add **s.**

one dish, two dish**es**
one dress, many dress**es**
one chick, three chick**s**

---

1 At the zoo we saw some
seal   seals

_____ .

2 We like to eat fresh
peach   peaches

_____ .

---

3 We have toys in three
box   boxes

_____ .

4 June will use a hair
brush   brushes

_____ .

---

5 Ed's mom gave him a
cap   caps

_____ .

6 Just look at those
dog   dogs

_____ .

---

7 Look at those shiny
star   stars

_____ .

8 The box was used for
mitten   mittens

_____ .

▶ Here's what to do!

Read each shopping list. Finish each word by adding the ending **s** or **es**.
Print it on the line.

Steve's List

1) 2 book_____ to read

2) 3 paintbrush_____

3) 6 red pencil_____

4) 2 jar_____ of paste

Peggy's List

1) 5 block_____

2) 2 box_____ of clay

3) 3 top_____ to spin

4) 2 puzzle_____

Pam's List

1) 8 dish_____

2) 8 cup_____

3) 4 glass_____

4) 2 patch_____ for jeans

Ron's List

1) 7 apple_____

2) 5 peach_____

3) 4 sandwich_____

4) 2 bunch_____ of grapes

Lesson 65: Plural endings -S, -ES

Name _____

Kim looked and looked for her clock.
Now she's looking for her sock.

 Give this a try!

Add **ing** to each base word. Print the new word on the line.

A **base word** is a word to which the ending **ing** or **ed** can be added to form a new word.

look + **ed** = look**ed**
look + **ing** = look**ing**

1 sleep _____

2 jump _____

3 play _____

4 help _____

5 start _____

6 work _____

7 fish _____

8 turn _____

 Now try this!

Add **ing** to the word beside each sentence. Print the word on the line.

9 We are _____ for the bus. | **wait**

10 Doris and Mark are _____ rope. | **jump**

11 Sam is _____ for the bus. | **look**

12 Bart's dog is _____ with him. | **stay**

13 Terry is _____ his lunch. | **hold**

14 Meg is _____ a book. | **read**

15 Now the bus is _____ our corner! | **turn**

Add **ed** to each base word. Print the new word on the line. Use the new words to finish the sentences.

1 look **2** want **3** help

_____ _____ _____

4 leap **5** fix **6** paint

_____ _____ _____

7 Jess _____ me catch a frog.

8 We _____ a frog for a pet.

9 We _____ everywhere for frogs.

10 Suddenly a frog _____ over a rock.

11 We_____up a box for a frog home.

> **Now try this!**

Print each base word on the line.

12 locked **13** marched **14** dreamed

_____ _____ _____

15 played **16** cleaned **17** passed

_____ _____ _____

18 watched **19** wanted **20** missed

_____ _____ _____

Name _____

▶ **Give this a try!**

Add **es** or **ed** to the base word in the box to finish each sentence.
Print the word on the line.

① The girls _____ baseball after school.

| play |

② Randy always watches and _____
for Jean's team to win.

| wish |

③ The ball comes fast and _____ past
Jean's bat. Strike one!

| brush |

④ The pitcher throws and the ball _____
toward the plate.

| buzz |

⑤ Jean swings as the ball _____ by.

| pass |

⑥ This time Jean has not _____ .

| miss |

⑦ Randy _____ up out of his seat.

| jump |

⑧ He _____ until he was hoarse.

| cheer |

▶ **Now try this!**

Add **s** or **es** to each base word in the box. Print the new word on the line.

| see | fox | bush | patch | mail | line |

⑨ _____   ⑩ _____

⑪ _____   ⑫ _____

⑬ _____   ⑭ _____

▶ Here's what to do!

Circle the word that will finish each sentence. Print it on the line.

1 Dad goes _____ in the stream in the woods.

fishing
fished

2 While the time _____, he looks around.

passes
passing

3 Yesterday some quacking ducks

_____ by.

floats
floated

4 Three baby ducks _____ their mother.

followed
following

5 Frogs were _____ in and out of the water.

jumping
jumps

6 They were _____ for bugs to eat.

looking
looked

7 Some birds were _____ each other.

helped
helping

8 While one _____ the nest, the other looked for food.

watched
watching

9 They _____ to feed their hungry babies.

needs
needed

10 Dad _____ looking around as much as he likes fishing.

liking
likes

Name _____

Do it this way!

Add **ing** to the base word in the box. Print it on the line.

When a short-vowel word ends in a single consonant, usually double the consonant before adding **ing**.
stop + ing = stopping

1. Maria and Jess were _____ to go shopping.

   | **plan** |

2. First they went _____ in the park.

   | **jog** |

3. Children were _____ on the swings.

   | **swing** |

4. Some horseback riders were

   _____ around.

   | **trot** |

5. Other people were _____ along a path.

   | **walk** |

6. They saw two bunnies _____ by.

   | **hop** |

7. A turtle was _____ at a bug.

   | **snap** |

8. A man was _____ hot dogs.

   | **roast** |

9. His dog was _____ for one.

   | **beg** |

10. "_____ in the park was fun," said Maria.

    | **Run** |

11. "Now let's go _____ ," Jess said.

    | **shop** |

Here's what to do!

Add **ed** to the word beside each sentence to make it tell about the past. Print the word on the line.

To make a word tell about the past, usually add **ed**. If a short vowel word ends in a single consonant, usually double the consonant before adding **ed**. I **skip** on my way home. Yesterday I **skipped** on my way home.

1 My dog _____ his tail when I got home.　　| **wag** |

2 He _____ up on me with a happy smile.　　| **hop** |

3 When I _____ him, my hand got muddy.　　| **pat** |

4 "Wags, you need to be _____!"　　| **scrub** |

5 I _____ him up.　　| **pick** |

6 Then I _____ him in the tub.　　| **dip** |

7 He _____ around in the water.　　| **jump** |

8 He _____ water everywhere!　　| **splash** |

9 I laughed as I _____ him.　　| **watch** |

10 When Wags _____, he was clean but I was a mess!　　| **stop** |

11 I _____ up the mess.　　| **clean** |

12 Then I _____ with Wags.　　| **play** |

138 Lesson 68: Inflectional ending -ED; doubling the final consonant

Name _____

▶ Here's what to do!

Circle the word that finishes each sentence. Print it on the line.

If a word ends with a silent **e**, drop the **e** before adding **ing** or **ed**.
I **bake** cookies with my mom.
We **baked** cookies yesterday.
We are **baking** cookies today, too.

(1) Yesterday I _____ to the park.

jogged
jogging

(2) Then I _____ home.

walked
walking

(3) Today I am _____ with friends.

skating
skated

(4) We are _____ for lunch.

stopped
stopping

▶ Now do this!

Read each pair of sentences. Add **ing** or **ed** to the base word. Print the word on the line.

(5) **clean**   Today Dad is _____ the garage.

He _____ the car yesterday.

(6) **save**   I am _____ my money to buy a bike.

Last week I _____ almost $3.00.

(7) **wag**   Last night my dog was happy, so she

_____ her tail.

She is _____ her tail now, too.

Add **ing** to each base word. Print the new word on the line.

1
ride _____

2
fry _____

3
rub _____

4
hide _____

5
frame _____

6
dig _____

7
take _____

8
jump _____

9
poke _____

10
ship _____

11
pack _____

12
quit _____

▶ **Now try this!**

Add **ed** to each base word. Print the new word on the line.

13
pin _____

14
rock _____

15
chase _____

16
hop _____

17
march _____

18
bake _____

19
wish _____

20
drop _____

21
hope _____

22
quack _____

▶ Do it this way!

Add the ending in the box to each word below it. Print the new words.

ing	ed	s or es
① wave	④ skip	⑦ peach
② drop	⑤ like	⑧ pass
③ smile	⑥ press	⑨ tree

▶ Now do this!

Finish each sentence by adding the correct ending to the base word in the box. Print the new word on the line

⑩ I like _____ all kinds of books. | **read** |

⑪ Yesterday I _____ a good storybook at the library. | **spot** |

⑫ I also _____ out a cookbook. | **check** |

⑬ It _____ you how to cook. | **teach** |

⑭ I _____ a pie after I read it. | **bake** |

⑮ My brother is _____ his money. | **save** |

⑯ He _____ every joke book he sees. | **get** |

Do it this way!

Add **ed** or **ing** to the words in the box. Use the new words to finish the sentences.

bake	come
have	help
plan	cut

1 Our grandparents are _____ over for dinner.

2 We are _____ to have pizza and salad.

3 We _____ the pizza first.

4 Now Carl is _____ vegetables for the salad.

5 Lisa _____ make the dessert.

6 We're _____ fun!

Now do this!

Draw a box around each base word.

7 d r e s s e d   **8** b u z z e s   **9** c o o k e d

10 p l a y s   **11** p u f f e d   **12** b r u s h i n g

13 d r i v e s   **14** l o a d i n g   **15** b o x e s

16 d i s h e s   **17** s n a p p i n g   **18** p a r k i n g

19 w i s h e d   **20** s t a y e d   **21** s w i m m i n g

Name _____

▶ **Here's what to do!**

Add an ending from the box to finish the word in each sentence.
Print it on the line. Trace the whole word.

ly	ful	less	ness

1. Polly was usually brave and ___fear_____ .

2. Today she was ___lone_____ in her new school.

3. She thought of her old friends with ___sad_____ .

4. She remembered all their
   ___kind_____ .

5. ___Sudden_____ she saw
   some girls smiling at her.

6. Now she felt more ___cheer_____ .

▶ **Now do this!**

Read the words in the box. Print each word below its definition.

fearless	darkness	safely	playful

7. with no fear

8. full of play

9. in a safe way

10. being dark

▶ Do it this way!

Add the ending in each box to the base words. Print the new words on the lines.

ly

1. quiet _____
2. glad _____

ful

5. use _____
6. skill _____

less

3. help _____
4. fear _____

ness

7. dark _____
8. black _____

▶ Now do this!

Add an ending to the base word in the box to finish each sentence. Print the new word on the line.

9. Owls like the _____ of night. | dark |

10. In the _____ they can hunt. | black |

11. They are _____ hunters. | skill |

12. Their sharp eyes are _____. | use |

13. They fly _____ with no sound. | quiet |

14. After a long night, owls fly

_____ home. | safe |

15. Then they _____ nap all day. | glad |

148 Lesson 73: Test: Suffixes -LY, -FUL, -LESS, -NESS

Name _____

The first dog is small,
But the next one is smaller.
Do you know which one is
smallest?

▶ Here's what to do!

Add the ending **er** and **est** to each word.
Print the new words on the lines.

You can add the ending **er** to a base word to make a new word that tells about two things. Add the ending **est** to tell about more than two things.

small   small**er**   small**est**

er	est

1. near _____ _____

2. long _____ _____

3. fast _____ _____

4. dark _____ _____

5. thick _____ _____

6. deep _____ _____

7. soft _____ _____

▶ Now do this!

Draw a picture to show the meaning of each word.

8. | 9. | 10.

long   longer   longest

Give this a try!

Finish each sentence by adding **er** or **est** to each base word. Use **er** to tell about two things. Use **est** to tell about more than two things. Print the word on the line.

1 tall

Meg is _____ than Jay.

2 hard

The rock is _____ than the soap.

3 fast

The horse is the _____ of the three.

4 long

The top fish is the _____.

5 cold

Ice is _____ than water.

6 small

The ant is the _____.

Name _____

▶ Give this a try!

Add **er** and **est** to each word. Print the new words on the lines.

When a word ends in **y** after a consonant, change the **y** to **i** before adding **er** or **est**.
busy + **est** = **busiest**

er		est

1. silly _____ _____

2. happy _____ _____

3. windy _____ _____

4. fluffy _____ _____

▶ Now try this!

Finish each sentence by adding **er** or **est** to the base word in the box.

5. Today was Justin's _____ kind of day. | happy |

6. He got to the bus stop _____ than he did yesterday. | early |

7. It was _____ than it had been all week. | sunny |

8. He made up the _____ joke he could. | silly |

9. The other kids said it was the | funny |

_____ one they had heard.

 **Give this a try!**

Circle the name of each picture.

When a word ends in **y** after a consonant, change the **y** to **i** before adding **es**.

story + **es** = stor**ies**

1

daisy   daisies

2

cherry   cherries

3

lily   lilies

 Now do this!

Use the rule to add **es** to the word beside each sentence. Finish the sentence by printing the new word on the line.

4 We wrote _____ for our class book. | story

5 Mine was about my dog's new _____ . | puppy

6 Lily wrote about planting _____ . | daisy

7 Penny's story was about raising _____ . | bunny

8 Carol told us about picking _____ . | cherry

9 Marty gave ideas for birthday _____ . | party

10 Jerry told how to take care of _____ . | pony

11 Tony wrote about his collection of _____ . | penny

12 When we finished, we made extra _____ . | copy

Name _____

1   bunny   **2**   city   **3**   box

_____   _____   _____

4   lily   **5**   dress   **6**   pony

_____   _____   _____

▶ **Now do this!**

Circle the word that will finish each sentence. Print it on the line. Then print the name of each picture.

7 Mary's birthday _____ was fun.
            (party,   parties)

8 Her dad read scary _____ in the dark.
            (story,   stories)

9 We tried to toss _____ into bottles.
            (penny,   pennies)

10 Instead of cake, we ate _____ pie.
            (cherry,   cherries)

11 Then we got little _____ to take home.
            (candy,   candies)

12   **13**   **14**

_____   _____   _____

Here's what to do!

Change the **y** to **i** and add **es** to the word in each box. Print the new words to finish the sentences.

1 Farms are different from _____. | city |

2 Sometimes my friends and our

_____ visit a farm. | family |

3 Sometimes there are lots of

_____ in the fields. | daisy |

4 Some _____ grow by the streams. | lily |

5 We like to ride the _____. | pony |

6 There are many different animal

_____. | baby |

7 It's fun to play with the _____. | bunny |

8 We usually see some _____. | puppy |

9 Fruits and _____ grow on farms. | berry |

10 We climb trees to pick _____. | cherry |

11 I like to write _____ about our trips to the country. | story |

12 I give_____ to my friends to read. | copy |

154 Lesson 76: Suffix -ES; words ending in Y

Name _____

Will you go sailing with me today?
The sun is shining, what do you say?

▶ **Do it this way!**

Find the word in the box that names each picture. Print it on the line.

In a **vowel pair,** two vowels come together to make one long vowel sound. When a word or syllable has a vowel pair, the first vowel stands for the long sound and the second vowel is silent. You can hear the long **a** sound in **sailing** and **today.**

sail	pay	rain
tail	hay	tray
spray	chain	nail

1
_____

2
_____

3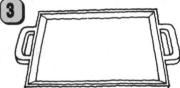
_____

4
_____

5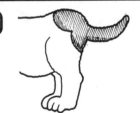
_____

6
_____

7
_____

8
_____

9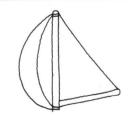
_____

▶ Here's what to do!

Find the word in the box that answers each riddle. Print it on the line.

chain	stain	mailbox	hay	pail	rain	tray
hair	paint	chair	train	gray	sail	day

1 I ride on railroad tracks. _____

2 You put letters in me. _____

3 I am a blend of black and white. _____

4 If I start, you put on a raincoat. _____

5 You can sit on me. _____

6 I am made of many links. _____

7 I am part of a boat. _____

8 I am an ink spot on a shirt. _____

9 I am piled in a stack. _____

10 You can use a comb on me. _____

11 You can carry water in me. _____

12 I am spread on a wall. _____

13 You carry food on me. _____

14 I come before night. _____

▶ Do it this way!

Circle the name of each picture.

Vowel pairs **ee** and **ea** can make the long **e** sound. You can hear the long **e** sound in **jeep** and **seal.**

1
sell
seal
seed

2
jeep
jeans
peep

3
bean
bed
bee

4
leaf
lean
leak

5
jeeps
jeans
jets

6
feed
feet
feel

7
deep
deeds
deer

8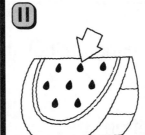
meat
met
team

9
eat
each
ear

10
peach
peace
pear

11
seal
seed
send

12
team
test
teeth

Here's what to do!

Find the word in the box that will finish each sentence. Print it on the line. Then print the two vowels that stand for its long **e** sound.

keep	eager	easy	meal	feet	steer
beaver	each	teeth	leaves	seem	seen

1 Have you ever _____ a beaver? _____

2 A _____ likes to chew down trees. _____

3 It makes a _____ of the bark. _____

4 It drags _____ branch home to
build a dam. _____

5 It only _____ the stump behind. _____

6 A beaver's _____ have to be strong. _____

7 Its webbed _____ help it swim along. _____

8 It uses its tail to _____ . _____

9 It's not _____ being a beaver. _____

10 Beavers always _____ to be working. _____

11 They _____ working until all their
work is done. _____

12 That's why busy people are often

called "_____ beavers." _____

158 Lesson 78: Vowel pairs EE, EA

Hide and Seek

This book belongs to _____

1

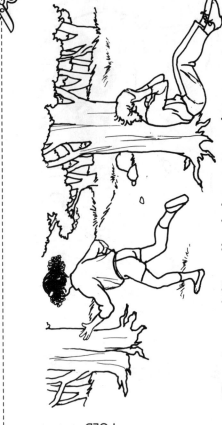

"Don't peek!" yelled Jean as she ran to find a hiding place.

"No way!" said Ray. He leaned against a tree and counted, "One, two, three . . ."

3

"I wish Ray would find me," thought Jean.

"I'm getting tired of waiting."

6

What is your favorite game to play? Draw a picture and write a sentence telling about it.

8

FOLD

FOLD

2

"Hi, Ray," said Jean, "Do you want to play on the train today?"
"No, I like playing hide and seek best," said Ray.
"Okay," said Jean. "You're it!"

4

"If I hide in the train he's sure to see me," thought Jean. "I know, I'll hide behind this tree."

5

The tree hid Jean so well, she couldn't see Ray.
She didn't hear Ray say, "Here I come."
"This sure is a neat hiding place," thought Jean.

7

Just then Jean took a peek. She didn't see Ray anywhere. Suddenly, she felt a tap on her shoulder. "You're it!" yelled Ray as he laughed and ran off to hide.

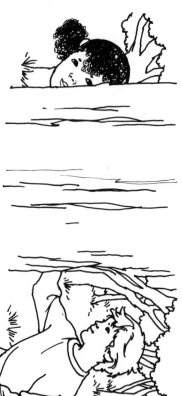

FOLD

FOLD

Name _____

▶ Do it this way!

Circle the word that will finish each sentence. Print it on the line.

The vowel pair **ie** sometimes has the long **i** sound. You can hear the long **i** sound in **tie.** The vowel pair **oe** has the long **o** sound. You can hear the long **o** sound in **hoe.**

1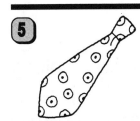

My dad, _____, and I went to the store.

jay
Joe
jot

2

Along the way, we saw a _____ by the road.

die
doe
day

3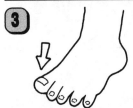

When we got there, Joe stubbed

his _____ .

tie
toe
lie

4

My dad needed to buy a new _____ .

hoe
hay
hit

5

I wanted to buy a new red _____ .

tie
toe
lie

6

We all had some _____ when we got home.

pie
pine
pile

▶ Give this a try!

Print the name for each picture on the line below it.

> The vowel pair **ow** sometimes has the long **o** sound. The vowel pair **oa** has the long **o** sound. You can hear the long **o** sound in **bowl** and **boat**.

| boat | rainbow | goat | bow | soap | bowl |

1 _____

2 _____

3 _____

4 _____

5 _____

6 _____

▶ Now try this!

Circle the word that will finish each sentence. Print it on the line.

7 Isn't it fun to ride in a _____ ?   boot   boat

8 Sailboats move when the wind _____ .   blows   blues

9 You use oars to _____ some boats.   raw   row

10 Tugboats _____ other boats along.   tow   too

11 Steamboats use steam to _____ along the river.   float   floor

Name _____

Do it this way!

Find the word in the box that will finish each sentence. Print it on the line. Then circle the two vowels in the word that stand for the long vowel sound.

1. Farmer Gray shears his _____ .

2. He _____ the wool into his truck.

3. Then he _____ weeds in the garden.

4. Farmer Gray picks a ripe _____ for a snack.

5. He will pick a few more to make a _____ .

6. Then he will put a new coat of _____ on the shed.

7. He is ready to sleep at the end of the _____ .

| day |
| loads |
| paint |
| peach |
| pie |
| sheep |
| hoes |

Now do this!

Make a word that answers each riddle by adding beginning and ending consonants.

8. It is something warm to wear.   _oa_

9. A dog wags it.   _ai_

10. They need socks.   _ee_

11. Seven of them make a week.   _ay_

12. You have five of these on each foot.   _oe_

13. You can wear these around your neck.   _ie_

Lesson 81: Reviewing vowel pairs AI, AY, EE, EA, OA, IE, OE, OW   **163**

© MCP All Rights Reserved.

▶ **Here's what to do!**

Find the name of each picture in the box. Print it on the line.

hoe	pie	hay	tree	jeans	boat	bowl	daisy

1   **2**   **3**   **4**

_____ _____ _____ _____

5   **6**   **7**   **8**

▶ **Now do this!**

Find a vowel pair in the box that will finish the word in each sentence.
Print it on the line. Trace the whole word.

9 Joe had a very bad _____d_____ .

10 Nothing ___s___med__ to go right.

11 First the hose sprang a _____l___k____ .

12 Water began to _____fl_____ all over.

13 Then Joe got __s___ked__ .

14 Have you ever had a day like _____J_____ did?

ai
ay
ee
ea
ie
oa
oe
ow

1

My, You've Grown!

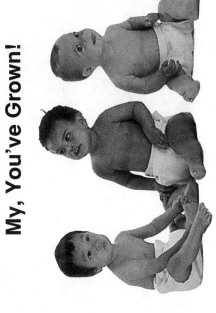

This book belongs to

_____

3

A baby horse, called a foal, tries to walk the day it's born.
At first, it won't roam far from its mother.
Later, the foal goes to find oats on its own.

8

[picture frame]

Paste your baby picture inside this picture frame.
Write one or two sentences telling what you were like as a baby.

6

A baby deer is called a fawn. Its mother is called a doe.
The mother protects her fawn from danger.

2

You've grown a lot from head to toe since you were born! All animals grow and change as they get older.

FOLD

4

A baby goat is called a kid. When it's full grown, it will have hollow horns and a beard.

FOLD

7

A baby dragonfly begins life underwater. When its outer skin splits open, it flies off into the sky!

5

A toad begins its life as an egg. Then it changes into a tadpole and finally into a toad.

Name _____

Look for me in the forest or in the zoo.
I have long fur, stripes, and a mask, too.
What am I?

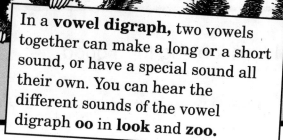

 Here's what to do!

Circle the word that will finish each
sentence. Print it on the line.

In a **vowel digraph,** two vowels
together can make a long or a short
sound, or have a special sound all
their own. You can hear the
different sounds of the vowel
digraph **oo** in **look** and **zoo.**

1 I felt something _____ in my mouth.

broom
loose

2 Was it a _____?

tool
tooth

3 I ran to my _____ .

room
zoo

4 I stood on a _____ to look in the mirror.

spoon
stool

5 My tooth should fall out _____ .

moon
soon

6 At _____ it was time for lunch.

soon
noon

7 I took a bite of _____ with my spoon.

food
fool

8 Out came my loose tooth on the _____ .

soothe
spoon

9 My friend lost a tooth, _____ .

too
zoo

Answer: A raccoon.

Lesson 83: Vowel digraph OO

167

► **Here's what to do!**

Find a word in the box that will finish each sentence. Print it on the line.

1 I was looking for a good _____.

2 I took a _____ at a cookbook.

3 I _____ in line to pay for the book.

4 Then I _____ my new book home.

5 I decided to _____ something.

6 I took my apron off a _____ and put it on.

7 I tried a _____ recipe.

8 The cookies were very _____.

cookie
book
look
cook
good
took
stood
hook

► **Now do this!**

Print the missing letters of each picture's name. Print the missing letters for a word that rhymes with it. Trace the whole word.

9

b _____
sh _____

10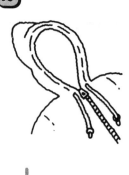

h _____
st _____

11

h _____
br _____

12

w _____
g _____

Name _____

►Here's what to do!
Find the word in the box that will finish each sentence. Print it on the line.

The vowel digraph **ea** can stand for the short **e** sound. You can hear the short **e** sound in **ready.**

1. When you wake up, take a deep

   _____ .

2. It will help clear your _____ .

3. Now you are ready for _____ .

4. Here is some _____ to make toast.

5. You can _____ butter and jam on it.

6. The eggs are _____ made.

7. Go _____ and eat.

ahead
already
breakfast
spread
bread
breath
head

►Now do this!
Circle the correct word to finish each sentence.

8. What is the (feather, weather, leather) like today?

9. Will you need to wear a (sweater, weather, meadow)?

10. Maybe you will need a (ready, heavy, cleanser) coat.

11. Is it cold enough for (bread, thread, leather) boots?

12. Cover your (head, heavy, breakfast) with a warm hat.

13. Now you are (meadow, heavy, ready) to go outside.

▶ **Do it this way!**

Say the name of each picture. Circle the words with the same **ea** sound as the picture's name.

1

seat
bread
meat
bean

2

bread
beach
heavy
treat

3

reach
steam
break
great

4

dream
mean
beak
health

5

head
heavy
lean
steak

6

steak
tea
teacher
great

7

beaver
team
leather
beans

8

bread
weather
seal
leather

9

ready
heavy
bread
bean

10

beach
teach
health
reach

11

break
leather
thread
weather

12

meat
great
heat
leak

Name _____

▶ **Here's what to do!**

Say the name of the first picture in each row. Fill in the bubble below
the picture with the same vowel sound.

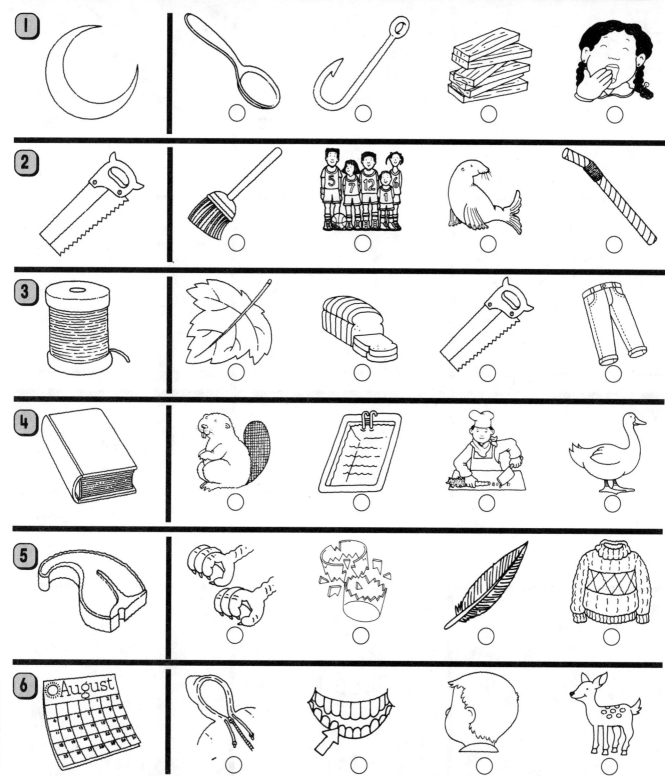

Here's what to do!

Say the name of each picture. Circle the letters that stand for the vowel sound in the picture's name. Then print the letters to finish its name. Trace the whole word.

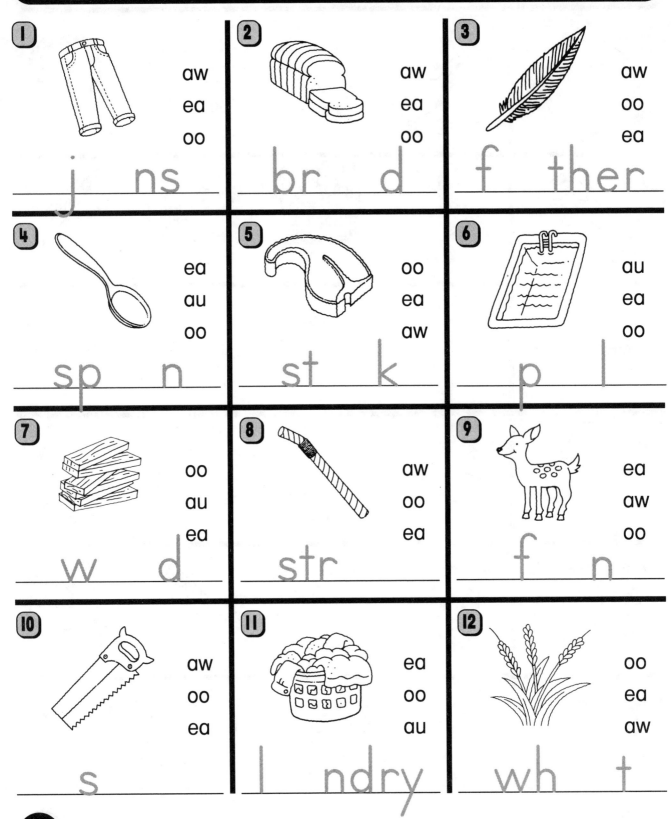

1
aw
ea
oo

j ___ ns

2
aw
ea
oo

br ___ d

3
aw
oo
ea

f ___ ther

4
ea
au
oo

sp ___ n

5
oo
ea
aw

st ___ k

6
au
ea
oo

p ___ l

7
oo
au
ea

w ___ d

8
aw
oo
ea

str ___

9
ea
aw
oo

f ___ n

10
aw
oo
ea

s ___

11
ea
oo
au

l ___ ndry

12
oo
ea
aw

wh ___ t

Lesson 86: Reviewing vowel digraphs OO, EA, AU, AW

Name _____

 Do it this way!

The answer to each riddle rhymes with the picture name. Find the answer in the box. Print it on the line.

toe	gray	pie	boat	spoon	bread	hook	saw

1 It rhymes with **book.**
You hang a coat on it.
What is it?

_____

2 It rhymes with **paw.**
You cut wood with it.
What is it?

_____

3 It rhymes with **doe.**
You have it on your foot.
What is it?

_____

4 It rhymes with **head.**
You can eat it.
What is it?

_____

5 It rhymes with **goat.**
You can row it.
What is it?

_____

6 It rhymes with **tie.**
Be sure to bake it.
What is it?

_____

7 It rhymes with **moon.**
You eat with it.
What is it?

_____

8 It rhymes with **hay.**
It names a color.
What is it?

_____

Lesson 87: Reviewing vowel pairs and vowel digraphs

175

Circle the word that will finish each sentence.

1. A baby deer is called a (seal, fawn, feather).
2. A low seat is called a (stool, school, steam).
3. A deep dish is called a (bean, book, bowl).
4. A dish under a cup is called a (saucer, saw, stool).
5. A crust filled with fruit is called a (pail, pea, pie).
6. A sharp tool to cut wood is called a (seam, saw, say).
7. A person who makes meals is called a (cook, shop, whale).
8. A kind of meat is called a (steam, steak, stoop).
9. A place where you swim is called a (paw, pear, pool).
10. Dried grass that horses eat is called (hay, ham, heat).

Now try this!

Print the missing letters to finish the name of each picture. Trace the whole word.

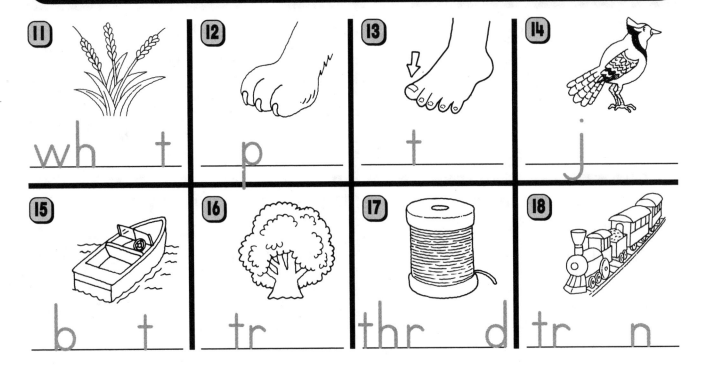

11. wh_ _t
12. _p_ _
13. _ _t
14. _ _j_
15. b_ _t
16. _tr_ _
17. thr_ _
18. d_ tr_ n

Autumn Is Coming

This book belongs to

1

Moose closes his book, gets ready, and then heads for Bear's house, too.

3

What do you think the other animals will do for the winter?
Write one or two sentences that tell what you think.

8

So on this night, they pause in their work to join together and say goodbye to the warm weather for a while.

6

2

Every year, on the night of the last full moon in August, Raccoon washes her paws and puts on her sweater.
Then she heads for Bear's house.

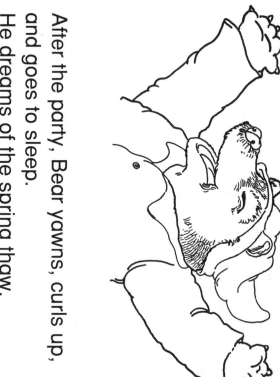

4

Hawk fluffs her feathers and polishes her claws.
She too heads for Bear's house.

— FOLD —

After the party, Bear yawns, curls up, and goes to sleep.
He dreams of the spring thaw.

7

— FOLD —

Why are the animals going to Bear's house?
Because autumn is coming.

5

Name _____

Doreen wears a round crown,
A velvet cape, and a gold gown.

▶ **Here's what to do!**

Say the name of the picture. Find its name in the list. Print its letter on the line below the picture.

A **diphthong** is made up of two letters blended together to make one sound. You can hear the sound of the diphthongs **ou** and **ow** in **round** and **crown.**

| 1 | | 2 | | 3 | |

___

4

a. clown   **j.** cow
b. cowboy   **k.** towel
c. mouse   **l.** flowers
d. shower   **m.** house
e. howl   **n.** town
f. owl   **o.** gown
g. now   **p.** pouch
h. crown   **q.** pout
i. cloud   **r.** mouth

5

6

7

8

9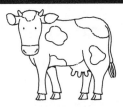

10

Here's what to do!

Read each sentence. Circle the **ou** or **ow** word in the sentence. Print it on the line.

1 I live on the edge of a small town.

_____

2 My house is near a farm.

_____

3 I spend a lot of time outdoors.

_____

4 From my yard I can see cows and horses.

_____

5 In summer, I watch the farmer plow his field.

_____

6 His tractor makes a loud noise.

_____

7 At night, I hear many different sounds.

_____

8 I can hear owls calling.

_____

9 I like to watch the clouds beyond the hills.

_____

10 In the fall, the flowers on the hill bloom.

_____

11 Today I saw a flock of birds flying south.

_____

12 They sense that winter is about to start.

_____

Name _____

 Give this a try!

Find a word in the box that answers each riddle. Print it on the line.

| owl | cow | flower | cloud | house | clown | plow | ground |

1 I am in the sky.
Sometimes I bring you rain.
What am I?

_____

2 I wear a funny suit.
I do many tricks.
I can make you smile.
What am I?

_____

3 I am in the garden.
I am very colorful.
I may grow in your yard, too.
What am I?

_____

4 You can plant seeds in me.
The farmer must plow me.
What am I?

_____

5 I am wide awake in the dark.
I hoot and howl.
What am I?

_____

6 You can see me at the farm.
I eat green grass.
I give you good milk.
What am I?

_____

7 You can live in me.
I will keep you warm and cozy.
What am I?

_____

8 The farmer uses me.
I help him make his garden.
What am I?

_____

Give this a try!

Print an X beside each word in which **ow** stands for the long **o** sound.

> Remember, **ow** can stand for the long **o** sound, as in **snow**, or it can make a sound of its own, as in **clown.**

1. _____ how
2. _____ snow
3. _____ own
4. _____ town
5. _____ crowd
6. _____ now
7. _____ bowl
8. _____ grow
9. _____ low
10. _____ plow
11. _____ power
12. _____ owl
13. _____ slow
14. _____ flow
15. _____ know
16. _____ show
17. _____ brown
18. _____ crow
19. _____ crown
20. _____ down
21. _____ towel
22. _____ glow
23. _____ throw
24. _____ brown
25. _____ cow
26. _____ blow
27. _____ arrow
28. _____ tower

Now try this!

Circle the **ow** word in each sentence. Print an X in the correct column to show which sound it makes.

	long vowel	diphthong
29. The circus came to our town.	_____	_____
30. We went to the show last night.	_____	_____
31. We sat in the very first row.	_____	_____
32. The star was a funny clown.	_____	_____
33. He made the crowd laugh.	_____	_____

Name _____

▶ **Give this a try!**

Circle the name of each picture.

> The diphthongs **oi** and **oy** usually stand for the same sound. You can hear that sound in **coin** and **boy**.

1

bow
boil
bill

2

boy
bag
toy

3

corn
coil
coins

4

sail
sell
soil

5
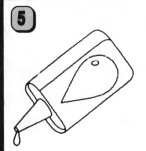
oak
oil
out

6

toil
tail
toys

7

paint
point
pail

8

noise
nail
nose

9
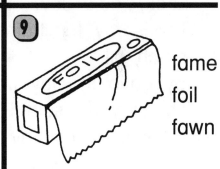
fame
foil
fawn

▶ **Now try this!**

Finish each sentence with a word from the box.

10 I have saved a few dollars and some _____ .

11 I will buy a _____ robot kit.

12 I will _____ putting it together.

| enjoy |
| toy |
| coins |

Here's what to do!

Read the story. Circle each **oi** word. Draw a box around each **oy** word.

The Runaway Toy

A boy named Roy had a birthday. His grandmother and grandfather gave him a choice of toys. Roy chose a toy train. He was a very happy boy.

Roy enjoyed his toy train, but it made too much noise. Roy took out a can of oil and oiled the toy. The oil made the train less noisy. It made it go faster, too.

One day Roy oiled it too much. The train went faster and faster. It raced around the room and out the door. Roy chased it out the door and down the path. The toy train rolled up to his sister, Joy.

"Look," said Joy. "This toy wants to join me outside."

"That's my toy train," said Roy. "It ran away from me. I used too much oil."

Joy gave the toy train to Roy.

"Thank you," said Roy. "From now on I will be more careful. I will not spoil my toy with too much oil."

Now do this!

Use the words you marked to answer the questions.

1 What was the boy's name? _____

2 What did he get for his birthday? _____

3 What made the train go fast? _____

4 What made Roy oil the train? _____

184 Lesson 91: Diphthongs OI, OY

Name _____

 Do it this way!

Find the word in the box that will finish each sentence. Print it on the line.

1. Floyd is a hungry _____.

2. He does not want to play with

   his _____.

3. Now he would _____ a bowl
   of popcorn.

4. _____ sister Joy wants
   popcorn, too.

5. Popcorn won't _____ their dinner.

6. Joy _____ Floyd in the kitchen.

7. Floyd pours some _____ in a pan.

8. _____ tells him to be careful.

9. The children listen for a popping _____.

10. Did Floyd and Joy make a good _____?

spoil
Joy
oil
choice
joins
noise
boy
enjoy
toys
Floyd's

Lesson 92: Diphthongs OI, OY **185**

Circle **yes** or **no** to answer each question.

1 Is a penny a coin?   Yes   No

2 Is <u>joy</u> being very sad?   Yes   No

3 Can you play with a toy?   Yes   No

4 Is oil used in a car?   Yes   No

5 Is a <u>point</u> the same as <u>paint</u>?   Yes   No

6 Can you boil water?   Yes   No

7 Can you make a choice?   Yes   No

8 Is a loud noise quiet?   Yes   No

Now try this!

Find the word in the box that will finish each sentence. Print it on the line.

9 _____ is glad the circus is in town.

10 She loves the _____ of the crowd.

11 The clown rides in a _____ car.

12 She smiles and _____ at the funny clown.

13 She sees a _____ standing up on a horse.

14 Nothing can _____ the day for Joyce.

15 Joyce always _____ a day at the circus.

spoil
enjoys
toy
Joyce
noise
points
boy

Name _____

 Here's what to do!

Find the word in the box that will finish each sentence. Print it on the line.

The diphthong **ew** stands for the long **u** sound. You can hear the long **u** sound in **new** and **few.**

1 I bought a _____ pack of sugarless gum.

2 I put a _____ pieces into my mouth.

3 I began to _____ the gum.

4 Then I _____ a giant bubble.

5 That bubble grew and _____ .

6 Suddenly, I _____ I was in trouble.

7 The bubble broke, and pieces

_____ everywhere.

8 I _____ the pieces of chewed gum away.

| grew |
| blew |
| chew |
| flew |
| new |
| threw |
| knew |
| few |

Now do this!

Print the missing letters for a word that rhymes with each word. Trace the whole word.

9 few

___st_____

10 crew

___thr_____

11 grew

___fl_____

1. (Drew, Blew, Knew) wanted a pet.
2. He went to (Crew, Dew, Flew) the Coop Pet Shop.
3. He saw puppies (chewing, stewing, mewing) on toy bones.
4. Baby birds (flew, stew, knew) around their cage.
5. They (few, threw, grew) seeds on the floor.
6. Drew really wanted a (mew, stew, new) kitten.
7. He saw a (chew, crew, grew) of kittens.
8. A (few, threw, grew) were very cute.
9. One kitten looked at him and (flew, mewed, chewed).
10. Drew (grew, dew, knew) he wanted that kitten.

11. Drew named him (Mews, Stews, Dews) because he always mewed.
12. That kitten (new, grew, chew) bigger every day.
13. Mews liked it when Drew (few, threw, mew) a toy to him.
14. He liked to (chew, new, stew) on Drew's shoestrings.
15. Mew tried to hide under the (screws, grew, newspaper).
16. From the window he watched birds as they (flew, crew, dew).
17. When the wind (blew, drew, stew), Mews chased fallen leaves.
18. He licked drops of morning (mew, dew, chew).
19. Before Drew (threw, few, knew) it, Mews was his friend.
20. Drew really loved his (stew, new, flew) pet.

Name _____

Circle the answer to each riddle.

1 You use it when you talk.
spoil   joy   soil   voice

2 It means that something is wet.
round   join   moist   oil

3 You see them do funny tricks.
crowns   clowns   browns   clouds

4 You can live in it.
house   plow   mouse   proud

5 It is something a dog can do.
howl   coin   stew   new

6 Very hot water can do this.
joy   boil   plow   oil

7 It is something to play with.
owl   toy   how   crowd

8 It is something we can eat.
mew   drew   stew   few

9 It means "not many."
new   few   dew   stew

10 It means "dirt."
soil   coil   boy   oil

11 The farmer uses it.
frown   plow   down   cloud

12 A cat likes to chase it.
house   out   shout   mouse

 Now do this!

Read the poem. Circle each **ow** word.

Chow Now?

"Moo—Moo," said Ms. Cow.
"How about some chow?
I want some now!"

"Not now, dear Ms. Cow.
Before you chow,
You help me plow!"

Lesson 94: Reviewing diphthongs   **189**

Finish each sentence with a word that rhymes with the word in the box. Print it on the line.

1. Girls and boys can shout with _____. | toy

2. A shout is one sound a _____ can make. | choice

3. Animals' voices make different _____. | pounds

4. Lions can roar with a powerful _____. | prowl

5. Wolves can _____ at the moon. | fowl

6. A _____ makes a little squeak. | house

7. Cows make a loud _____ when they moo. | poise

8. These are just a _____ voice sounds. | dew

9. _____ many others can you think of? | Now

Now do this!

Read each sentence. Circle each **oi** or **oy** word.

Troy enjoys toys.

Troy enjoys noise.

So Troy enjoys toys

That make a loud noise.

All About Clouds

This book belongs to

_____

Look up at the sky.
What kind of clouds do you see?
Draw a picture of them and write a
sentence that tells what they may bring.

_____
_____
_____

8

1

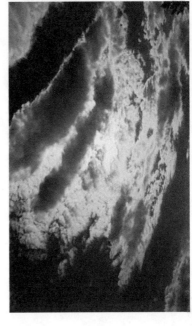

Has it been boiling hot for days now?
If you see clouds like these, you may
soon hear the noisy sound of thunder
and be drowning in rain!

3

A sky like this is called a "mackerel sky."
The clouds look like fish scales.
If you see them, count on the weather
changing.

6

2

Weather maps and clouds can tell us what the weather will be for the next few hours or days.

Here's how to tell if the weather will be enjoyable or annoying.

4

Are the clouds as gray as oysters?

Is it so dark it looks as if someone drew the curtains closed?

Snow or rain may be coming your way.

FOLD

7

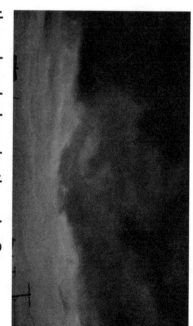

Are the clouds low in the sky?

If you live in the mountains, clouds like these may cover the ground like mist or dew.

FOLD

5

Warm air rises from the ground to make these clouds.

Go ahead and enjoy a picnic.

These clouds won't spoil a sunny day with rain.

Name _____

Today, I'll pack a snack in a paper sack.
Tomorrow, I'll repack that sack with another snack.

The prefix **re** usually means **do again**.

repack
The prefix is **re**.
The base word is **pack**.
I'll **repack** the sack.

►Here's what to do!

Add **re** to the word beside each sentence. Use the new words to finish the sentences.

1 Every day I do things that I have

to _____ .

| do |

2 When I get up, I _____ my bed.

| make |

3 I _____ my teeth after I eat.

| brush |

4 I _____ my backpack before school.

| pack |

5 I _____ my shoes.

| tie |

6 When my camera needs film,

I _____ it.

| load |

7 I read and _____ my favorite books.

| read |

8 I write and _____ my stories.

| write |

9 Every night I _____ my alarm clock.

| wind |

Here's what to do!

Add **un** to the word beside each sentence. Use the new words to finish the sentences.

When the prefix **un** is added, the new word means the opposite of the original word.
Keys can **lock.** Keys can **unlock.**
unlock
The prefix is **un.**
The base word is **lock.**

1. Every day we do things and _____ them. | do |

2. We dress and _____ . | dress |

3. We button and _____ our clothes. | button |

4. We tie our shoes and then _____ them. | tie |

5. We lock and _____ doors to go in and out. | lock |

6. We buckle our seat belts and _____ them. | buckle |

7. We wrap up our lunches and then

   _____ them. | wrap |

8. We pack our backpacks and _____ them. | pack |

9. We load film in a camera and later _____ it. | load |

10. I am not _____ about all this undoing. | happy |

11. It just seems a little _____ to me. | usual |

12. But it's probably _____ things will ever change. | likely |

Name _____

 Do it this way!

Add **re** or **un** to the word beside each sentence. Use the new word to finish the sentence.

1 Last night my baby sister _____ my backpack.

packed

2 She tried to _____ my homework with her crayon.

do

3 I have to _____ my story.

write

4 Now I _____ my backpack every night.

check

5 I am very _____ about it, too.

happy

6 My things are _____ around my sister.

safe

 Now do this!

Print one word that means the same as each pair of words.

7
not cooked _____

8
spell again _____

9
not safe _____

10
use again _____

11
not able _____

12
play again _____

13
not kind _____

14
tell again _____

Do it this way!

Add the prefix **un** or **re** to each underlined word. Print the new word on the line.

1 to <u>read</u> again

_____

2 opposite of <u>lock</u>

_____

3 to <u>fill</u> again

_____

4 opposite of <u>tie</u>

_____

5 opposite of <u>buckle</u>

_____

6 to <u>heat</u> again

_____

7 to <u>build</u> again

_____

8 opposite of <u>pack</u>

_____

9 to <u>write</u> again

_____

10 opposite of <u>happy</u>

_____

11 to <u>play</u> again

_____

12 to <u>wind</u> again

_____

Name _____

▶ Give this a try!

Add **dis** to each word. Use the new words to finish the sentences.

disorder
The prefix is **dis**.
The base word is **order**.

1 My dog Wags _____ for a while.

appeared

2 Then I _____ my shoe was missing.

covered

3 "Why did you _____ me Wags?"

obey

4 "You know I'm _____ when you take my things."

pleased

5 "That was a _____ thing to do."

loyal

6 "Wags, you are a _____."

grace

7 Wags barked to _____ .

agree

8 He pulled my shoe out of my _____ toy chest.

orderly

Fill in the bubble beside the word that will finish each sentence. Write it on the line.

1

Mr. Fixit will

_____

the plug before fixing the telephone.

○ discolor
○ disconnect

2

The rider will

_____

and let her horse rest.

○ dismount
○ distaste

3

Meg and Peg are twin sisters, but

they _____
on many things.

○ disagree
○ disappear

4

The puppy

_____ its
owner and ran outside with her hat.

○ dishonest
○ disobeyed

5

Will loves green beans, but he

_____

eggplant.

○ dislikes
○ disgrace

6

Kirk made the dirt appear, so he
had to make it

_____.

○ disappear
○ distrust

Name _____

 Here's what to do!

Add **un, dis,** or **re** to each base word to make a new word. Print it on the line.

un or dis	re or dis

1 _____ agree   **2** _____ happy   **7** _____ able   **8** _____ writes

3 _____ obey   **4** _____ easy   **9** _____ add   **10** _____ like

5 _____ lucky   **6** _____ please   **11** _____ pay   **12** _____ loyal

Now do this!

Add **un, dis,** or **re** to each underlined word to change the meaning of the sentence. Print the new word on the line.

13 Grandpa was <u>pleased</u> about the plans for his party.

_____

14 He said he felt <u>easy</u> about getting gifts.

_____

15 Sadly Sue <u>wrapped</u> the present she had made.

_____

16 Then Jake said they would <u>obey</u> Grandpa just once.

_____

17 With a grin, Sue <u>wrapped</u> the gift.

_____

18 She <u>tied</u> the bow.

_____

19 Grandpa was not <u>happy</u> with his party after all.

_____

Circle the prefix that makes sense in the sentence. Write the prefix on the line.

1 I stopped to _____ load my camera at the zoo.　　　　dis　re

2 I _____ placed it in my camera bag.　　　　re　un

3 I _____ covered a large rhino looking at me.　　　　re　dis

4 It seemed to be friendly, but I felt _____ easy.　　　　un　dis

5 I was _____ sure what it might do.　　　　dis　un

6 I know that may be _____ fair.　　　　re　un

7 I don't mean to make the rhino _____ happy.　　　　un　re

8 I'm not trying to be _____ kind.　　　　re　un

9 It's just that I _____ trust huge animals.　　　　dis　un

10 It would be _____ honest to say it didn't scare me.　　　　re　dis

11 A rhino could _____ able me with its huge horn.　　　　un　dis

12 I _____ agree with people who say a rhino is harmless.　　　　dis　re

13 That huge beast looks really _____ safe to me.　　　　re　un

14 I hope they remembered to _____ check the lock.　　　　re　dis

15 I know I would _____ like seeing a rhino out of its cage.　　　　un　dis

16 I wish I had _____ read my books about rhinos.　　　　re　dis

Name _____

I see a large, white cloud in the sky.
It looks so big floating way up high.

Do it this way!

Print each word from the box beside
a word that means the same thing.

Synonyms are words that have the
same or almost the same meaning.
Large and **big** mean the same thing.

| glad | ill | damp | fast | little | large |

1 big _____

2 small _____

3 happy _____

4 quick _____

5 sick _____

6 wet _____

Now do this!

Circle the word in each row that means almost the same thing as the
first word.

7	**jolly**	sad	big	happy	jump
8	**junk**	gems	trash	list	top
9	**pile**	heap	near	rest	stop
10	**sleep**	awake	nap	paint	read
11	**sick**	ill	quick	lazy	glad
12	**quick**	step	slow	pony	fast
13	**sound**	sad	noise	find	happy
14	**large**	huge	many	tiny	blue
15	**close**	move	let	shut	see

Finish Peggy's letter. Print a word from the box that means the same thing as the word below each line.

friend	gifts	noise	fast	hope	kind	laugh
happy	races	easy	big	little	enjoy	

Dear Pablo,

I'm _____ that you came to my party. It was
         (glad)

_____ of you to bring _____. The
  (nice)   (presents)

_____ book looks _____ to read. I will
  (large)   (simple)

_____ reading it. When I wind up the
  (like)

_____ robot, it _____ _____
  (small)   (runs)   (quickly)

and makes a funny _____. It makes me
         (sound)

_____ to watch it. Thank you very much. I
  (giggle)

_____ to see you soon.
  (wish)

Your _____ ,
      (pal)

Peggy

Name _____

I have a cute little dog named Paul.
His ears are big and his nose is small.

Here's what to do!

Find a word in the box that means the opposite of each word. Print its letter on the line.

Antonyms are words that are opposite or almost opposite in meaning. **Big** and **small** mean the opposite of each other.

a. old	**b.** wet	**c.** start	**d.** full	**e.** slow
f. last	**g.** down	**h.** hot	**i.** good	**j.** short
k. out	**l.** well	**m.** few	**n.** winter	**o.** long
p. far	**q.** lower	**r.** shallow	**s.** shut	**t.** awake
u. thick	**v.** fat	**w.** white	**x.** hard	

1 ____ dry   **2** ____ up   **3** ____ summer   **4** ____ short

5 ____ near   **6** ____ fast   **7** ____ tall   **8** ____ bad

9 ____ cold   **10** ____ thin   **11** ____ sick   **12** ____ many

13 ____ stop   **14** ____ upper   **15** ____ first   **16** ____ deep

17 ____ new   **18** ____ empty   **19** ____ open   **20** ____ in

21 ____ asleep   **22** ____ easy   **23** ____ black   **24** ____ skinny

▶ Do it this way!

Print a word from the box that means the opposite of each word.

stop	open	full	ill	cry	night
float	hot	strong	asleep	sit	smile

1 awake

_____

2 closed

_____

3 empty

_____

4 cold

_____

5 healthy

_____

6 stand

_____

7 weak

_____

8 sink

_____

9 day

_____

10 laugh

_____

11 frown

_____

12 go

_____

Name _____

What do you say to a knight before he goes to bed?

Give this a try!

Find a word in the box that sounds the same as each word below. Print it on the line.

Homonyms are words that sound alike but have different spellings and meanings. **Knight** and **night** are homonyms.

tail	here	to	road	pail	heal
blue	week	cent	sail	maid	sea

1 heel _____

2 see _____

3 rode _____

4 sent _____

5 tale _____

6 blew _____

7 weak _____

8 pale _____

9 hear _____

10 two _____

11 sale _____

12 made _____

Now try this!

Circle the word that will finish each sentence. Print it on the line.

13 Maggie _____ her horse into the woods.   road   rode

14 Her puppy wagged its _____ and ran along.   tail   tale

15 They saw a _____ that hid behind a tree.   dear   deer

16 Maggie watched the _____ set in the West.   son   sun

Answer: Night, knight!

Find a word in the box that sounds the same as each word below. Print it on the line.

son	meat	blew	to	pane	tow	tale	week
heel	wait	beet	cent	sea	dear	sew	

1 weight _____

2 sun _____

3 weak _____

4 sent _____

5 blue _____

6 beat _____

7 deer _____

8 two _____

9 heal _____

10 pain _____

11 see _____

12 meet _____

13 so _____

14 tail _____

15 toe _____

▶ **Now try this!**

Use words from the box and the activity above to finish the sentences.

16 It had rained all _____.

17 When Pete woke up, the _____ was shining.

18 He could _____ his friends playing outside.

19 He pulled on his _____ jeans in a hurry.

20 After breakfast, he ran out _____ play.

Name _____

Print **S** on the line between words that mean the same thing. Print **O** on the line between words that mean the opposite.

1 first _____ last

2 little _____ small

3 under _____ over

4 hard _____ soft

5 like _____ enjoy

6 stop _____ go

7 creep _____ crawl

8 bad _____ good

9 big _____ large

10 pretty _____ ugly

11 bug _____ insect

12 float _____ sink

13 loud _____ noisy

14 present _____ gift

15 day _____ night

Now try this!

Find the word that sounds like each word. Print its number on the line.

16
maid _____ **1.** sun
son _____ **2.** seem
seam _____ **3.** made

17
week _____ **1.** tail
pail _____ **2.** pale
tale _____ **3.** weak

18
pair _____ **1.** sea
see _____ **2.** pear
beet _____ **3.** beat

19
pain _____ **1.** pane
blew _____ **2.** in
inn _____ **3.** blue

20
deer _____ **1.** two
too _____ **2.** heel
heal _____ **3.** dear

21
rode _____ **1.** ring
here _____ **2.** road
wring _____ **3.** hear

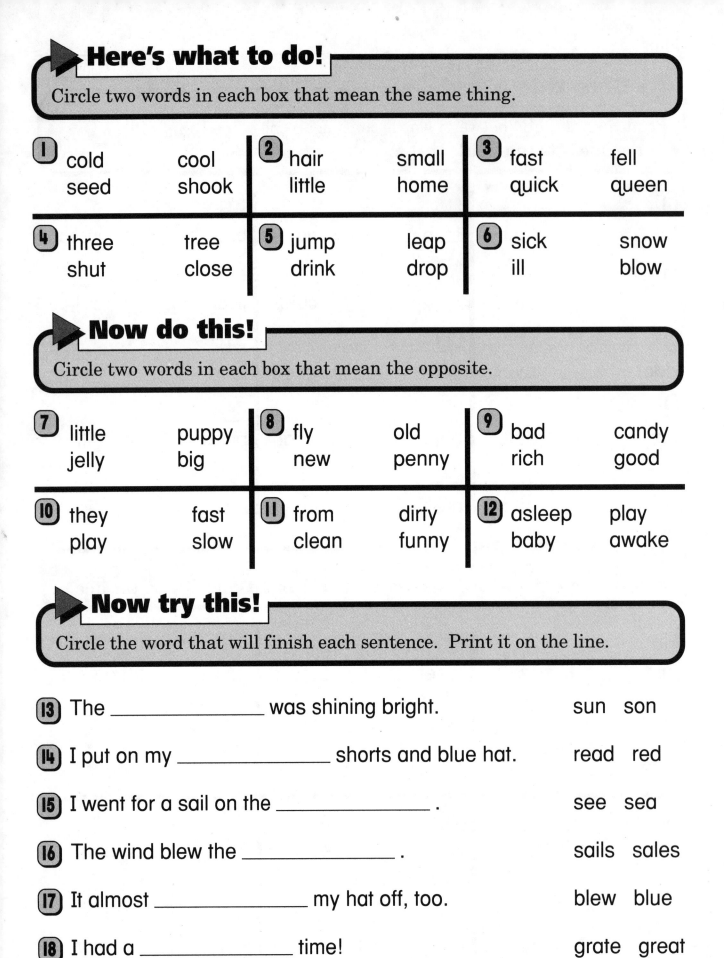

Here's what to do!

Circle two words in each box that mean the same thing.

1 cold   cool
     seed   shook

2 hair   small
     little   home

3 fast   fell
     quick   queen

4 three   tree
     shut   close

5 jump   leap
     drink   drop

6 sick   snow
     ill   blow

Now do this!

Circle two words in each box that mean the opposite.

7 little   puppy
     jelly   big

8 fly   old
     new   penny

9 bad   candy
     rich   good

10 they   fast
     play   slow

11 from   dirty
     clean   funny

12 asleep   play
     baby   awake

Now try this!

Circle the word that will finish each sentence. Print it on the line.

13 The _____ was shining bright.   sun   son

14 I put on my _____ shorts and blue hat.   read   red

15 I went for a sail on the _____ .   see   sea

16 The wind blew the _____ .   sails   sales

17 It almost _____ my hat off, too.   blew   blue

18 I had a _____ time!   grate   great